So you really want to learn

Maths

Book 3

Answer Book

Serena Alexander B.A. (Hons.), P.G.C.E.

Edited by Louise Martine B.Sc. (Lon.)

GALORE PARK

www.galorepark.co.uk

Published by Galore Park Publishing Ltd.
19/21 Sayers Lane, Tenterden, Kent TN30 6BW
www.galorepark.co.uk

Typography and layout by Typetechnique, London W1
Cover design by GKA Design, London WC2H
Printed by Charlesworth Press, Wakefield

ISBN: 978 1 902984 35 3

First published 2005
Reprinted 2008, 2009, 2011

Details of other Galore Park publications are available at www.galorepark.co.uk

ISEB Revision Guides, publications and examination papers may also be
obtained from Galore park.

Preface

The publishers would like to once again thank David Hanson of the ISEB for his invaluable help during the production of this book. Serena and all of us at Galore Park are most grateful.

Contents

Chapter 1: Working with numbers

Exercise 1.1

1.	35	11.	40	21.	75
2.	72	12.	63	22.	41
3.	159	13.	6	23.	25
4.	6	14.	25	24.	36
5.	21	15.	35	25.	39
6.	21	16.	16	26.	43
7.	24	17.	46	27.	16
8.	98	18.	3	28.	24
9.	4	19.	56	29.	124
10.	21	20.	40	30.	270

31.	180	41.	45	51.	180
32.	18	42.	5	52.	24
33.	16	43.	15	53.	169
34.	86	44.	114	54.	225
35.	315	45.	171	55.	225
36.	2	46.	121	56.	225
37.	55	47.	198	57.	500
38.	63	48.	792	58.	10 000
39.	210	49.	180	59.	40
40.	86	50.	360	60.	1250

Exercise 1.2

1.	972	6.	23	11.	14 697
2.	1363	7.	43	12.	27
3.	4183	8.	37	13.	30 659
4.	6188	9.	42	14.	29
5.	8928	10.	43	15.	27

Exercise 1.3: Solving problems

1. 8760 hours
2. 525 600 minutes; 31 536 000 seconds
3. 1568 ounces
4. 8 stones 6 pounds
5. 9680 yards
6. 4 miles and 960 yards
7. 2992 hamburgers
8. 440 pints
9. 22
10. (a) 368 sheets   (b) 15 min 20 sec
11. £12 480
12. 27 weeks

Exercise 1.4

1.	−7	**11.**	−12	**21.**	−5
2.	−3	**12.**	17	**22.**	4
3.	−3	**13.**	6	**23.**	−12
4.	16	**14.**	−12	**24.**	−2
5.	−9	**15.**	4	**25.**	−1
6.	−3	**16.**	−10	**26.**	−7
7.	−22	**17.**	−4	**27.**	5
8.	−21	**18.**	12	**28.**	16
9.	−4	**19.**	−5	**29.**	−3
10.	3	**20.**	25	**30.**	−10

Exercise 1.5

1. 5   17   37

2. 1   2   3   4   6   9   36

3. 12   24   36

4. 2   3   7

5. 2   5

6. 17

7. (a) 84   (b) 16   (c) 42

8. 31, 37, 41, 43, 47,

9. (a) 1, 5, 13, 65   (b) 1, 101   (c) 1, 19   (d) 1, 2, 3, 4, 6, 8, 9, 12, 18, 24, 36, 72

10. (a) $2^3 \times 3^2 \times 7$ (b) $2^3 \times 17$ (c) $2^3 \times 5^3$ (d) $3^3 \times 5 \times 7$

11. (a) 1, 2, 3, 4, 6, 8, 12, 24; 1, 2, 3, 6, 7, 14, 21, 42
       (b) 1, 2, 3, 6,
       (c) 6

12. (a) 2   (b) 10   (c) 20

13. 4, 8, 12, 16, 20, 24, 28, 32, 36, 40

14. 6, 12, 18, 24, 30, 36, 42, 48, 54, 60

15. 10, 20, 30, 40, 50, 60, 70, 80, 90, 100

16. (a) 12   (b) 20   (c) 30

17. (a) 40   (b) 60   (c) 1800

Exercise 1.6

1. (a) 63   (b) 8   (c) 5   (d) 1

2. 5

3. 33

4. 58

5. 200

6. 120

7. (a) 7560   (b) 8568   (c) 189 000   (d) 128 520

8. 11 550

9. 660

10. 8932

11. 180

12. (a) 28, 56, 84, 112   (b) 300

Exercise 1.7

1. Practical – just involves turning the calculator on.
2. 61
3. 22 008
4. 0.040 404 …
5. 18 817 344
6. −29
7.

1.	−7	11.	−12	21.	−5
2.	−3	12.	17	22.	4
3.	−3	13.	6	23.	−12
4.	16	14.	−12	24.	−2
5.	−9	15.	4	25.	−1
6.	−3	16.	−10	26.	−7
7.	−22	17.	−4	27.	5
8.	−21	18.	12	28.	16
9.	−4	19.	−5	29.	−3
10.	3	20.	25	30.	−10

8. (a) 45   (d) −10
   (b) 54   (e) 2
   (c) 26   (f) 0.2

9. (a) 380   (b) 81   (c) 52   (d) 4

10. 24.6̇
11. −259.52
12. 0.543 961 352
13. 50.611 111 …
14. 0.231 733 634
15. 8.380 032 206
16. 42.421 052 63
17. 0.010 441 847

18. (a) 9   (b) 289   (c) 441   (d) 20 736
19. (a) 8   (b) 19   (c) 26   (d) 254
20. 0.125, 8, 0.125, 8 etc.

Exercise 1.8

1. 17, 34, 51, 68, 85, 102, etc.
2. 15, 16, 17, 18
3. 11, 12, 13
4. (a) A (4704)   (b) B (3039.75)   (c) B (2928)

5. (a) Too small, last digit should be 3
   (b) Too big, last digit should be 2
   (c) Too small, last digit should be 3 or 8
   (d) Last digit should be 9

6.   (a) $321 \times \mathbf{6}$ = 1926
       (b) 1234 **+ 692** = 1926
       (c) $80892 \div \mathbf{42}$ = 1926
       (d) $\mathbf{214} \times 9$ = 1926

7.   On the 10001th time you will have 100020001
8.   On the 1001th time you will have 1002001
9.   Yes 3
10.   SOB $80\{30^2 + 3 \times (106 - 69)\} = 80\,880$
       BOSS $4 \times \{9 \times (119 + 14) + 100\} = 5188$

       BIBI $\dfrac{50\,(26^2 - 13)}{13 \times 17} = 150$

       BOBBO $9^2(9^2 + 4^2 + 2^2) = 8181$
       ISIS $(29 + 16) \times (81 + 98) = 8055$

       ISO $\dfrac{135 \times 101}{3 \times 9} = \text{SOS}$

       EARTH $5 \times (26 + 42) + 25 \times (29 + 18) = 1515$

       SIBB $\dfrac{100^2 + 3 \times 30^2}{\sqrt{625}} = 508$

       Earth to **ISIS** to **BOSS** to **SIBB** to **SOB** to **BOBBO** to **BIBI** and finally to **ISO** where the message is **SOS**.
11.   524 288
12.   About 168 900 000 km (nearly 170 million), obviously impossible!

Exercise 1.9: Extension questions

1.   0.04
2.   (a) 5   (b) 12.5   (c) 25
3.   1
4.   (a) 25   (b) 100   (c) 100
5.   4, 0.25, 4 , 0.25 etc.
6.   Most are recurring decimals - but $\dfrac{1}{77}$ and $\dfrac{1}{121}$ are very interesting:

$\dfrac{1}{11}$	$0.\dot{0}\dot{9}$	$\dfrac{1}{55}$	$0.0\dot{1}\dot{8}$	$\dfrac{1}{99}$	$0.\dot{0}\dot{1}$
$\dfrac{1}{22}$	$0.0\dot{4}\dot{5}$	$\dfrac{1}{66}$	$0.01\dot{5}$	$\dfrac{1}{110}$	$0.00\dot{9}\dot{0}$
$\dfrac{1}{33}$	$0.\dot{0}\dot{3}$	$\dfrac{1}{77}$	$0.\dot{0}1298\dot{7}$	$\dfrac{1}{121}$	$0.008\,264\,462\,81\,...$
$\dfrac{1}{44}$	$0.02\dot{2}\dot{7}$	$\dfrac{1}{88}$	$0.0113\dot{6}$	$\dfrac{1}{132}$	$0.007\dot{5}$

7. $\dfrac{1}{3}, \dfrac{1}{5}, \dfrac{1}{15}$

8. $\dfrac{18}{25}$

9. 1, 0.5, 0.667, 0.6. 0.625, 0.615, 0.619, 0.618, 0.618, 0.618

10. (a) $\dfrac{1}{5}$ full

    (b) (i) $\dfrac{3}{10}$ full   (ii) $\dfrac{3}{5}$ full

    (c) Just over 3 minutes (3 minutes 20 seconds) or $3\dfrac{1}{3}$ minutes

    (d) $\dfrac{xy}{x+y}$

11. The tank will fill in 3 min 36 sec so hopefully the intergalactic traveller managed to get his mask on first, although he may have had to hold his breath once the water level came over his mouth.

Exercise 1.10: Summary exercise

1.	85	**6.**	86
2.	24	**7.**	432
3.	96	**8.**	29
4.	12	**9.**	444
5.	193	**10.**	23

11. (a) −11   (f) −5
    (b) 11   (g) −75
    (c) 12   (h) −3
    (d) −7   (i) −12
    (e) 8   (j) 3

12. 5, 13, 31
13. 1, 2, 4, 7, 14, 28
14. 6, 12, 30
15. (a) 8   (b) 42
16. (a) 40   (b) 1848
17. Yes, 2579 kg
18. (a) 2068 kg
    (b) 22 days ($22\dfrac{1}{2}$ days almost)

19.	−11.105 263 16	**22.**	222
20.	0.25	**23.**	0.615 2777
21.	−30	**24.**	1.295 731 707

End of chapter 1 activity: Calculator puzzles and games

Guess the number
See if the pupils can uncover why this puzzle works.

Down to zero
This exercise tests the pupils' observations on factors. If they can divide then they will get their number down to zero more quickly.

Countdown
This game is just like the TV game.

Finding remainders
This game uses the same methods pupils should have used in Exercise 1.3
The instructions spell out exactly the method they have to follow.

Calculating Easter
This puzzle requires some stamina but it does work. (Hopefully your pupils will be too exhausted to ask you why!)

Remember it works out Saturdays, so one day less than the following:

Easter Day			
	2011 – April 24	2021 – April 4	2031 – April 13
	2012 – April 8	2022 – April 17	2032 – March 28
	2013 – March 31	2023 – April 9	2033 – April 17
2004 – April 11	2014 – April 20	2024 – March 31	2034 – April 9
2005 – March 27	2015 – April 5	2025 – April 20	2035 – March 25
2006 – April 16	2016 – March 27	2026 – April 5	2036 – April 13
2007 – April 8	2017 – April 16	2027 – March 28	2037 – April 5
2008 – March 23	2018 – April 1	2028 – April 16	2038 – April 25
2009 – April 12	2019 – April 21	2029 – April 1	2039 – April 10
2010 – April 4	2020 – April 12	2030 – April 21	2040 – April 1

Chapter 2: Decimals

This chapter briefly revises decimal arithmetic, but the problems now involve two or more stages. It is recommended that a calculator is not used for the first nine exercises. However using a calculator to check these answers is a useful way to reinforce its correct use.

Exercise 2.1

1.	£2.78	6.	£1.17
2.	£15.24	7.	£2.57
3.	£65.55	8.	£4.67
4.	£39.55	9.	24p each
5.	£9.93	10.	£8.84

Exercise 2.2

1.	0.24	6.	0.044
2.	0.03	7.	0.078
3.	0.000 12	8.	1.56
4.	0.21	9.	0.6
5.	0.1	10.	0.96
11.	1.68	16.	24
12.	1.08	17.	0.66
13.	7	18.	0.1407
14.	0.2	19.	0.002
15.	15	20.	0.0915

Exercise 2.3

1.	60	6.	4
2.	0.6	7.	4000
3.	50	8.	0.07
4.	30	9.	3000
5.	0.6	10.	30 000
13.	3.4	18.	0.67
14.	0.0034	19.	267
15.	640	20.	0.002
16.	67	21.	800
17.	40 000	22.	0.009

Exercise 2.4: More money problems

1.	£54	4.	£23.40
2.	£3.80	5.	£5.90
3.	£6.42	6.	42p

7. £1.47
8. 22, 10p
9. £19.62
10. £61.95

11. £5.40
12. £2.90
13. £10.86 if I had an ice-cream, £10.05 if I didn't.
14. £3.20

Exercise 2.5

1. 20 cl
2. 80 boys
3. 600 000
4. Both 14 km (14 000 m)
5. 54.6 cm
6. 500 ml of shampoo costing £2.25 (45p per ml rather than 50p per ml)
7. 1500 km
8. 3
9. 2382 mm
10. 640 litres

Exercise 2.6

1. 0.1 m by 10 m,   0.4 m by 2.5 m,   0.25 m by 4 m,
    0.125 m by 8 m,   0.8 m by 1.25 m,   0.5 m by 2 m
    (other answers are possible)

2. 0.1 m by 20 m,   0.2 m by 10 m,   0.25 m by 8 m,
    0.4 m by 5 m,   0.8 m by 2.5 m, (other answers are possible)
3. 8 m
4. 0.2 cm
5. 0.3 m
6. 0.24 m²
7. 4cm
8. 5.333 or $5\frac{1}{3}$ cm

9. 1000 cm (10 m)
10. 1920 cm (1.92 m)

Exercise 2.7

These questions and their answers are intended to be a starting point for discussion.

1. 0.22 m, so 22 cm
2. 8, 8 and 9
3. About 133 ml
4   9 days
5. 11 days (if he takes only one weekend)
6. If the sand is divided equally then each house will get just over 833 kg. But it does not say equal so the amount could vary.

7. 3 metres
8. 221 ml
9. 1.6 million
10. £67.15

Exercise 2.8

1. (a) 500	(b) 516.2	(c) 516	(d) 516.153
2. (a) 0.14	(b) 0.14	(c) 0.1365	(d) 0.1365
3. (a) 9	(b) 9.4	(c) 9.36	(d) 9.357
4. (a) 0.08	(b) 0.1	(c) 0.08 328	(d) 0.0833
5. (a) 2	(b) 2.0	(c) 2.00	(d) 2.000
6. (a) 11	(b) 10.9	(c) 10.91	(d) 10.909

Exercise 2.9

Pupils should give their estimates first and then calculate the accurate answers using their calculators.

1.	5,	4.81	7.	0.3,	0.312 905 287
2.	6000,	6214.285 714	8.	600,	530.380 5543
3.	0.05,	0.052 3269	9.	0.005,	0.005 470 504
4.	0.02,	0.022	10.	400,	508.767 5993
5.	600,	590.931 3362	11.	300,	343.217 5199
6.	3000,	3629.125 874	12.	2,	2.255 270 769

Exercise 2.10: Summary exercise

1. £4.42
2. (a) 0.12   (b) 0.03   (c) 0.036   (d) 0.02
3. (a) 50   (b) 5   (c) 40   (d) 60
4. 14 litres (or 15 litres)
5. 1 m by 1.5 m,   0.5 m by 3 m,   0.3 m by 5 m,
   0.1 m by 15 m,   0.15 m by 10 m, (other answers are possible)

6. (a) 0.22 m²   (b) 800 cm

7. (a) (i) 4.25   (ii) 4.255
   (b) (i) 12.05   (ii) 12.046
   (c) (i) 4.01   (ii) 4.010

8. (a) (i) 140 000   (ii) 143 000
   (b) (i) 0.046   (ii) 0.0457
   (c) (i) 50 000   (ii) 50 000

9. (a) (i) 4   (ii) 100 (to 1 s.f.)
   (b) (i) 4.398 751 982   (ii) 114.734 9134

End of chapter 2 activity: The national elf problem

(a) 2

(b) 6

(c) 16

(d) If $x = y$ then there are x elves.

If y is a factor of x then there are x elves.

Otherwise there are $x + y - f$ elves in general. Where f is the highest common factor of x and y.

9 by 6	9 + 6 = 15	HCF 3	Number of elves 12	(15 − 3)
4 by 6	4 + 6 = 10	HCF 2	Number of elves 8	(10 − 2)
12 by 8	12 + 8 = 20	HCF 4	Number of elves 16	(20 − 4)
15 by 12	15 + 12 = 27	HCF 3	Number of elves 24	(27 − 3)

Chapter 3: Fractions

For those pupils who are interested, there is plenty to research about Egyptians and their fractions.

The Horus fractions are considered 'magic' but your pupils are probably more familiar with the magic number $9\frac{3}{4}$. In several exercises one answer is $9\frac{3}{4}$, it could be a special challenge to find them all!

Exercise 3.1

1.   (a) $\frac{1}{4} = \frac{2}{8}$ (b) $\frac{12}{16} = \frac{3}{4}$ (c) $\frac{2}{5} = \frac{4}{10}$ (d) $\frac{9}{24} = \frac{3}{8}$

2.   (a) $9\frac{3}{4}$ (b) $2\frac{2}{5}$ (c) $3\frac{1}{2}$ (d) $10\frac{2}{3}$

3.   (a) $\frac{21}{5}$ (b) $\frac{15}{4}$ (c) $\frac{39}{5}$ (d) $\frac{22}{7}$

4.   (a) $\frac{3}{5}$ (b) $\frac{2}{3}$ (c) $\frac{7}{18}$ (d) $\frac{3}{7}$

5.   (i) (a) 0.15   (b) 0.24   (c) 0.56   (d) 1.25

     (ii) (a) $\frac{3}{20}$ (b) $\frac{6}{25}$ (c) $\frac{14}{25}$ (d) $1\frac{1}{4}$

6.   (i) (a) $\frac{7}{20}$ (b) $1\frac{9}{25}$ (c) $\frac{2}{25}$ (d) $\frac{1}{8}$

     (ii) (a) 35%   (b) 136%   (c) 8%   (d) 12.5%

7.   (i) (a) 0.4   (b) 0.56   (c) 0.65   (d) 0.625
     (ii) (a) 40%   (b) 56%   (c) 65%   (d) 62.5%

8.   (a) $\frac{1}{5}$ (b) $\frac{3}{10}$ (c) $\frac{7}{40}$ (d) 7.5%   (e) 9%   (f) 12.5%

Adding Fractions

When adding and subtracting fractions some teachers still teach their pupils to 'make them improper fractions first'. This does work but can give some very unwieldy numbers, making such calculations without a calculator very difficult.

Do encourage pupils to look for **lowest** common denominators and not just multiply the two denominators together.

Exercise 3.2

1. $\dfrac{13}{15}$

2. $\dfrac{7}{8}$

3. $1\dfrac{1}{28}$

4. $1\dfrac{1}{9}$

5. $1\dfrac{11}{36}$

6. $\dfrac{37}{40}$

7. $4\dfrac{11}{12}$

8. $6\dfrac{4}{15}$

9. $5\dfrac{31}{35}$

10. $7\dfrac{4}{5}$

11. $7\dfrac{15}{16}$

12. $3\dfrac{3}{10}$

13. $8\dfrac{13}{72}$

14. $5\dfrac{8}{15}$

15. $8\dfrac{11}{18}$

16. $10\dfrac{11}{42}$

17. $9\dfrac{5}{42}$

18. $7\dfrac{1}{24}$

19. $6\dfrac{2}{5}$

20. $4\dfrac{73}{112}$

21. $7\dfrac{25}{42}$

22. $9\dfrac{3}{4}$

23. $7\dfrac{25}{42}$

24. $13\dfrac{41}{60}$

Subtraction

'Borrowing' with fractions needs careful explanation and reminders, even for the brightest students. Most will understand the **principle of decomposition**, but you may like to introduce this method as well:

Example:

$$5\dfrac{4}{9} - 2\dfrac{5}{6} = 3\dfrac{8-15}{18} \qquad 8-15 \text{ is } -7$$

$$= 3 - \dfrac{7}{18} \qquad \text{Take } \dfrac{7}{18} \text{ from } 3$$

$$= 2\dfrac{11}{18}$$

Exercise 3.3

1. $\frac{5}{12}$

2. $\frac{3}{20}$

3. $\frac{5}{24}$

4. $\frac{1}{4}$

5. $\frac{1}{14}$

6. $\frac{7}{30}$

7. $2\frac{8}{35}$

8. $3\frac{7}{15}$

9. $3\frac{1}{20}$

10. $1\frac{4}{63}$

11. $2\frac{7}{20}$

12. $1\frac{43}{45}$

13. $2\frac{7}{12}$

14. $\frac{10}{21}$

15. $2\frac{22}{35}$

16. $\frac{7}{10}$

17. $2\frac{2}{15}$

18. $\frac{8}{9}$

19. $2\frac{1}{6}$

20. $1\frac{5}{6}$

21. $2\frac{5}{36}$

Mixed addition and subtraction
Remind the pupils of the BIDMAS rule.

Exercise 3.4

1. $\frac{31}{60}$

2. $\frac{23}{45}$

3. $1\frac{1}{20}$

4. $\frac{13}{60}$

5. $\frac{9}{20}$

6. $\frac{71}{84}$

7. $1\frac{13}{60}$

8. $\frac{1}{20}$

9. $\frac{11}{60}$

10. $\frac{53}{60}$

11. $1\frac{23}{60}$

12. $\frac{5}{8}$

13. $\frac{1}{40}$

14. $3\frac{31}{40}$

15. $9\frac{3}{4}$

16. $2\frac{19}{20}$

17. $1\frac{47}{60}$

18. $\frac{11}{20}$

A fraction of an amount

The concept is simple enough for questions 13 to 23. The pupils will need to use the correct cancellations to get the correct answers quickly. This is a good exercise to do before going on to multiplication. It also provides a little revision of units.

Exercise 3.5

1.	5	5.	54
2.	6	6.	65
3.	12	7.	115
4.	30	8.	57.6

9. 120 cm
10. 80 minutes
11. 2250 grams
12. 3 km 500 m

13.	170	17.	60.5
14.	133	18.	136
15.	225	19.	80.5
16.	75	20.	99

21. 2 hours 30 minutes
22. 4800 mm
23. 25 seconds

Exercise 3.6

1. $\dfrac{4}{7}$ 4. $\dfrac{9}{50}$ 7. $\dfrac{4}{21}$

2. $\dfrac{2}{7}$ 5. $\dfrac{1}{6}$ 8. $\dfrac{6}{35}$

3. $\dfrac{1}{6}$ 6. $\dfrac{2}{9}$ 9. $\dfrac{1}{9}$

Exercise 3.7

1. $\dfrac{1}{2}$ 5. 2 9. $3\dfrac{3}{7}$

2. $\dfrac{3}{5}$ 6. $1\dfrac{5}{8}$ 10. $3\dfrac{5}{8}$

3. $\dfrac{4}{5}$ 7. 3 11. 3

4. 2 8. $4\dfrac{46}{49}$ 12. $8\dfrac{1}{4}$

Exercise 3.8

1. $\dfrac{8}{45}$

2. $\dfrac{3}{50}$

3. $\dfrac{8}{35}$

4. $\dfrac{1}{21}$

5. $\dfrac{4}{105}$

6. $\dfrac{3}{20}$

7. $\dfrac{1}{12}$

8. $\dfrac{1}{20}$

9. $\dfrac{11}{150}$

10. $\dfrac{1}{18}$

11. $4\dfrac{2}{3}$

12. $10\dfrac{5}{12}$

13. 16

14. 12

15. $9\dfrac{3}{4}$

16. 4

17. $42\dfrac{13}{144}$

18. $388\dfrac{4}{5}$

Exercise 3.9

1. $\dfrac{7}{8}$

2. $\dfrac{2}{3}$

3. $1\dfrac{1}{9}$

4. $2\dfrac{11}{12}$

5. $\dfrac{7}{10}$

6. $3\dfrac{3}{4}$

7. $1\dfrac{1}{3}$

8. $\dfrac{3}{4}$

9. $7\dfrac{1}{5}$

10. $2\dfrac{2}{3}$

11. $2\dfrac{5}{14}$

12. $1\dfrac{1}{3}$

Exercise 3.10

1. $\dfrac{1}{3}$

2. 5

3. $\dfrac{1}{x}$

4. $1\dfrac{1}{3}$

5. $1\dfrac{1}{6}$

6. $9\dfrac{3}{4}$

7. $\dfrac{2}{3}$

8. $\dfrac{3}{10}$

9. a

10. $\dfrac{y}{x}$

11. $\dfrac{x}{5}$

12. x^2

Exercise 3.11

1. 6

2. $\dfrac{11}{12}$

3. $2\dfrac{1}{10}$

4. $1\dfrac{11}{12}$

5. $9\dfrac{3}{4}$

6. $1\dfrac{1}{17}$

7. 24

8. $1\dfrac{1}{5}$

9. $1\dfrac{1}{5}$

10. $2\dfrac{2}{5}$

11. $2\dfrac{5}{8}$

12. $3\dfrac{6}{7}$

13. 3

14. 3

15. 3

16. $3\dfrac{1}{15}$

17. $2\dfrac{2}{9}$

18. $\dfrac{32}{55}$

Exercise 3.12

1. $2\dfrac{13}{15}$

2. $\dfrac{5}{7}$

3. $\dfrac{1}{2}$

4. $4\dfrac{17}{70}$

5. $2\dfrac{1}{8}$

6. $\dfrac{15}{61}$

7. $\dfrac{37}{40}$

8. $\dfrac{5}{8}$

9. $9\dfrac{3}{4}$

10. $2\dfrac{80}{111}$

11. $\dfrac{2}{5}$

12. $2\dfrac{8}{37}$

Exercise 3.13

These answers are the same as those in Exercises 3.1 – 3.10 but done on the calculator. You might suggest that pupils use their calculators to find other calculations where the answer is $9\dfrac{3}{4}$

Exercise 3.14: Extension questions 1

1. $\dfrac{63}{64}$

2. $\dfrac{1}{64}$

3. (a) $\dfrac{1}{4}$ (b) $\dfrac{1}{8}$ (c) $\dfrac{1}{16}$ (d) $\dfrac{1}{32}$

4. (a) $\dfrac{1}{16}$ (b) $\dfrac{1}{8}$ (c) $\dfrac{1}{64}$ (d) $\dfrac{1}{4}$

5. Note that:

$\dfrac{1}{4} + \dfrac{1}{4} = \dfrac{1}{2}$ is allowed but $2 \times \dfrac{1}{4} = \dfrac{1}{2}$ is not.

There are many different answers. You could get pupils to check each others' answers by using a calculator.

6. (a) $\dfrac{1}{2} + \dfrac{1}{8}$ (b) $\dfrac{1}{2} + \dfrac{1}{16}$ (c) $\dfrac{1}{2} + \dfrac{1}{8} + \dfrac{1}{32}$ (d) $\dfrac{1}{4} + \dfrac{1}{8} + \dfrac{1}{64}$

7. (a) $\dfrac{1}{4} \div \left(\dfrac{1}{2} + \dfrac{1}{4} \right)$ (c) $\left(\dfrac{1}{4} + \dfrac{1}{8} + \dfrac{1}{16} \right) \div \left(\dfrac{1}{2} + \dfrac{1}{16} \right)$

(b) $\left(\dfrac{1}{4} + \dfrac{1}{8} \right) \div \left(\dfrac{1}{2} + \dfrac{1}{8} \right)$ (d) $\left(\dfrac{1}{4} + \dfrac{1}{16} + \dfrac{1}{32} \right) \div \left(\dfrac{1}{2} + \dfrac{1}{8} + \dfrac{1}{32} \right)$

8. Find the smallest multiple of 2 that is larger than a or b. Then the calculation will be:

$$\dfrac{a}{2^n} \div \dfrac{b}{2^n}$$

You then need to find a number of different multiples of 2 which add up to a and b. This is where a table might help.

Exercise 3.15: Extension questions 2 – Continued fractions

It would be quite a good idea to look more closely at the Chinese fraction. Not only would this serve as a reminder about the value of pi, but it is quite an interesting arithmetic exercise.

You could talk about: 3, 7, 15, 1, 292 and then break the fraction down into stages:

Stage 1: $\qquad 3 + \dfrac{1}{7} = \dfrac{22}{7} = 3.142\ 857\ 143$

Stage 2: $\qquad 3 + \cfrac{1}{7 + \cfrac{1}{15}} = \dfrac{333}{106} = 3.141\ 509\ 434$

Stage 3: $\qquad 3 + \cfrac{1}{7 + \cfrac{1}{15 + \cfrac{1}{1}}} = \dfrac{355}{113} = 3.141\ 592\ 920$

Stage 4: $\qquad 3 + \cfrac{1}{7 + \cfrac{1}{15 + \cfrac{1}{1 + \cfrac{1}{292}}}} = \dfrac{103993}{33102} = 3.141\ 592\ 653$

You can see how at each stage the decimal answer becomes closer to the true value of pi (3.141592654 to 9 d.p.).

The interesting point in this, for those that find such things interesting, is to derive the fraction and thus the continued fraction series.

The trick in deriving continued fractions is to:

1. Keep dividing numbers into the integer part and fraction part.
2. Invert the fraction part and, when inverting, remember that for instance $17 = \dfrac{1}{\frac{1}{17}}$

This is how you work it backwards for pi:

First consider π to 8 decimal places 3.141 592 65

$$\pi = 3.141\ 592\ 65$$

$$= 3 + 0.141\ 592\ 65$$

$$= 3 + \cfrac{1}{1/(0.141\ 592\ 65)}$$

$$= 3 + \cfrac{1}{7.062\ 513\ 485}$$

$$= 3 + \cfrac{1}{7 + \cfrac{1}{1/(0.062\ 513\ 485)}}$$

$$= 3 + \cfrac{1}{7 + \cfrac{1}{15.996\ 548\ 58}}$$

$$= 3 + \cfrac{1}{7 + \cfrac{1}{15 + \cfrac{1}{1/(0.996\ 548\ 58)}}}$$

Pupils who wish to pursue this further, could find the continued fraction sequence for $\sqrt{2}$, and other roots.

An interesting appendix to this is that the fraction $\dfrac{355}{113}$ is a very good approximation of pi (useful to know when your pupils have lost their scientific calculator and have to resort to one of those you keep for the 'juniors'.)

To remember this result, just write the first 3 odd numbers, and repeat each one: 1 1 3 3 5 5

Divide in the middle, 1 1 3   3 5 5, swap them around: 3 5 5   1 1 3, insert a fraction bar and you

have $\dfrac{355}{113}$

After that little diversion let us return to the answers for this exercise:

1. (a) (i) $1\frac{1}{2}$ (ii) $1\frac{2}{3}$ (iii) $1\frac{3}{5}$ (iv) $1\frac{5}{8}$ (v) $1\frac{8}{13}$

    (b) 1.5   1.6666 ...   1.6   1.625   1.1.$\overline{615384}$

    The pupils may spot that the patterns of the numerators (1, 2, 3, 5, 8) and the denominators (2, 3, 5, 8, 13) are numbers in the Fibonacci sequence. Depending on how far they then take the pattern it should converge around 1.618

2. (a) $1\frac{1}{3}$ (b) $1\frac{4}{9}$ (c) $1\frac{16}{37}$ (d) $1\frac{81}{187}$ (e) $1\frac{489}{1129}$

    This one is rather a disappointment; it looks as if you are going to get a numerator sequence of perfect squares, but then you do not!

    (f) However they do converge to about 1.433

3. (a) $1\frac{1}{2}$ (b) $1\frac{3}{4}$ (c) $1\frac{11}{16}$ (d) $1\frac{83}{120}$ (e) $1\frac{1267}{1832}$

    (f) These converge to about 1.7

4. Check pupils' own work.

5. Check pupils' own work.

Exercise 3.16: Summary exercise

1. (i) (a) $\frac{6}{25}$ (b) $1\frac{7}{20}$ (c) $\frac{1}{8}$

    (ii) (a) 24%   (b) 135%   (c) 12.5%

2. (i) (a) 0.6   (b) $0.\dot{6}$ (c) 1.85

    (ii) (a) 60%   (b) $66\frac{2}{3}$%   (c) 185%

3. (a) $1\frac{13}{30}$ (b) $3\frac{13}{24}$ (c) $9\frac{3}{4}$

4. (a) $\frac{13}{18}$ (b) $9\frac{3}{4}$ (c) $\frac{11}{28}$

5. (a) $\frac{31}{70}$ (b) $3\frac{1}{30}$

6. 118

7. 2625 metres

8.   (a) $\dfrac{9}{20}$ (b) $\dfrac{1}{15}$ (c) $20\dfrac{1}{8}$ (d) $9\dfrac{3}{4}$

9.   (a) $1\dfrac{1}{3}$ (b) $1\dfrac{1}{2}$ (c) $9\dfrac{3}{4}$ (d) $1\dfrac{11}{13}$

10.   (a) $\dfrac{2}{5}$ (b) $9\dfrac{3}{4}$

11.   (a) $\dfrac{47}{50}$ (b) $\dfrac{1}{50}$

12 of the answers in this chapter were $9\dfrac{3}{4}$

End of chapter 3 activity:
Fraction, decimal and percentage dominoes

Practical

Chapter 4: Index numbers

Although the work in this chapter, on indices and roots, goes beyond the requirements of the syllabus, it does teach the students how to use a wide range of functions on their calculators. A better understanding of this will be of great benefit to all of them and they do enjoy it.

It is a good idea to do some work with square roots before they go on to Chapter 10 on Pythagoras' theorem. This section will familiarise them with squares and with roots and make them even more proficient with the relevant calculator functions.

The final section on calculating with square roots is strictly for scholars only.

A note on calculators

With the huge variety of models now on the market a maths teacher can waste a great deal of time showing individual students how to use their own. It can be a good idea to choose a model you approve of and organise a 'bulk buy'. That way you have to be familiar with only one model.

Exercise 4.1

1.   (a) 2^3 (b) 9^2 (c) 3^3 (d) 8^2 (e) 2^5 (f) 4^3

2.   (a) 8   (b) 81   (c) 27   (d) 64   (e) 32   (f) 64

3.   (a) 3^2 (b) 2^4 (or 4^2)   (c) 7^2 (d) 12^2 (or $2^4 \times 3^2$ or $3^2 \times 4^2$)
      (e) 3^5 (f) 7^3 (g) 11^3 (h) 13^2

Exercise 4.2

1.   (a) 3^5 (c) 6^{11} (e) 4^9
      (b) 7^7 (d) 3^5 (f) 7^5

2.   (a) 2^3 (c) 4^4 (e) 5
      (b) 7^4 (d) 3^3 (f) 7^2

3.   (a) 4^4 (c) 5^5 (e) 4^4
      (b) 7   (d) 3^3 (f) 7^4

4.   (a) 3^{10} (c) 7   (e) 2^0 (1)
      (b) 5^2 (d) 3^0 (1)   (f) 7^0 (1)

5.   (a) 3^6 (f) 4^4 (k) $6^5 \times 5^5$ (or 30^5)
      (b) 8^3 (g) 2^7 (l) 5^7
      (c) $6^7 \times 5^5$ (h) $3^2 \times 5^3 \times 2^2$ (or $6^2 \times 5^3$)   (m) $4^8 \times 3^3 \times 5^2$
      (d) $7^2 \div 2^2$ (or $3\frac{1}{2}^2$)   (i) $7^6 \times 3^2$ (n) 6^{10}
      (e) $6^7 \div 5^2$ (j) 3^3 (o) 6^2

6. (a) 2×3^3 (c) 2×4^2 (e) 2×5^3
     (b) 2×7^2 (d) 2×5^2 (f) 2×7^3

7. (a) $2^3 + 3^3$ (c) 3×4^2 (e) 3×4^5
     (b) 7^0 (1)   (d) 5^3 (f) 3×7^3

Exercise 4.3

1. (a) 2^{-3} (b) 9^{-2} or 3^{-4} (c) 3^{-3} (d) 8^{-2} or 2^{-6} (e) 2^{-5} (f) 4^{-3} or 2^{-6}

2. (a) $\dfrac{1}{8}$ (b) $\dfrac{1}{81}$ (c) $\dfrac{1}{27}$ (d) $\dfrac{1}{64}$ (e) $\dfrac{1}{32}$ (f) $\dfrac{1}{64}$

3. (a) 3^{-2} (b) 2^{-4} or 4^{-2} (c) 7^{-2} (d) 12^{-2} (e) 2^{-7} (f) 3^{-3} (g) 6^{-3} (h) 5^{-4}

4. (a) 3^{-3} (c) 6^{-3} (e) 4^{-4}
     (b) 7^{-2} (d) 3^0 (1)   (f) 7^{-4}

5. (a) 2^3 (c) 4^{-4} (e) 5^{-1}
     (b) 7^4 (d) 3^3 (f) 7^{-2}

6. (a) 4^4 (c) 5^5 (e) 2^4
     (b) 7^{-3} (d) 3^1 (3)   (f) 7^0 (1)

7. (a) 3^0 (1)   (c) 6^{-2} (e) 4^{-1}
     (b) 4^4 (d) 3^7 (f) 7^{10}

Exercise 4.4: Solving Equations with x^2

1. $x = 1$ **5.** $y = 2$ **9.** $b = 0.4$
2. $a = 10$ **6.** $a = 8$ **10.** $y = 20$
3. $b = 7$ **7.** $x = 0.3$ **11.** $x = 0.01$
4. $c = 9$ **8.** $a = 40$ **12.** $s = 0.5$

Exercise 4.5

1. 4   **5.** 1.44   **9.** 0.01
2. 5   **6.** 0.5   **10.** 0.0001
3. 100   **7.** 12   **11.** 0.06
4. 0.16   **8.** 10000   **12.** 1.1

The following answers may be either fractions or decimals:

13. 2.25   **15.** 0.01 $\left(\dfrac{1}{100}\right)$ **17.** 0.2 $\left(\dfrac{1}{5}\right)$

14. 0.1   **16.** $\dfrac{1}{3}$ **18.** 0.25 $\left(\dfrac{1}{4}\right)$

19. $\dfrac{4}{9}$

21. 2

23. 0.8

20. $0.4 \left(\dfrac{2}{5}\right)$

22. $\dfrac{4}{9}$

24. 1

Exercise 4.6

1. $2^4 \times 3^2$, 12

2. $3^2 \times 5^2$, 15

3. $2^6 \times 3^2$, 24

4. $3^2 \times 13^2$, 39

5. $3^4 \times 5^2$, 45

6. $2^2 \times 7^2$, 14

7. $2^2 \times 3^4$, 18

8. $5^2 \times 7^2$, 35

9. $3^2 \times 11^2$, 33

10. $3^4 \times 7^2$, 63

11. $2^6 \times 7^2$, 56

12. $2^4 \times 3^2 \times 7^2$, 84

Exercise 4.7

1. 729

2. 1296

3. 5

4. 729

5. 4

6. 256

7. 3

8. 243

9. 3

10. 256

11. 2

12. 5

13. (a) 25   (b) 36   (c) 625
     76^2 which is 5776

14. 42, yes you always get the lower of the original numbers – even if the number is a fraction, but **not** if the number is a negative.

Exercise 4.8

1. (a) 25   (b) 225   (c) 529   (d) 15 625
2. (a) 5   (b) 17   (c) 24   (d) 512
3. 0.2, 5, 0.2, 5 and so on (if you covered the chapter on fractions then this should be familiar).
4. (a) 128   (b) 78 125   (c) 2401   (d) 1 048 576
5. (a) 6   (b) 12   (c) 20   (d) 125
6. (a) 2   (b) 3   (c) 4   (d) 5
7. 0.228 933 782 …
8. 0.941 123 948..   **11.** 2.695 398 602
9. 5300.727 308..   **12.** 2
10. 2.4

13. From Earth (11345) to Shell (0.553) to Esso (501734) to Helios (4518) to Bish (318808) to Bobbie (01134) to Hello (5151) to Isis (55178) where the message is Bliss!

(Reading the calculator upside down sounds odd but it is very clear when you actually do it. You could try and get the class to make their own words (they will anyway!) and then make them write calculations for each other to get these words. That should keep them quiet!)

Exercise 4.9

1. 10^4
2. 10^3
3. 10^{-3}
4. 10^{-6}
5. 10^{10}
6. 10^{-8}

7. 10^7
8. 10^{-5}
9. 10^9
10. 10^{-9}
11. 10^{-2}
12. 10^0

Exercise 4.10

1. 3×10^4
2. 4×10^{-5}
3. 9×10^{-2}
4. 6×10^{-4}
5. 7×10^{-8}
6. 8×10^7

7. 6×10^{-5}
8. 8×10^{-6}
9. 7×10^3
10. 6×10^{-15}
11. 7×10^5
12. 3×10^{10}

Exercise 4.11

1. 200
2. 0.000 06
3. 700 000 000
4. 5000
5. 0.000 0007
6. 0.000 003

7. 90 000
8. 0.03
9. 6 000 000
10. 80 000 000
11. 0.0009
12. 70 000 000 000

Exercise 4.12

1. 2800
2. 490
3. 365 000
4. 9 360 000
5. 0.1001

6. 0.005 68
7. 0.000 909
8. 0.031 42
9. 161 800
10. 0.007 205

Exercise 4.13

1. 3.9×10^3
2. 1.15×10^4
3. 5.6×10^7
4. 4.05×10^5
5. 3.9×10^4

6. 7.7×10
7. 8.09×10^{11}
8. 2.005×10^7
9. 6.075×10^5
10. 9.08×10^6

11. 5×10^{-3}

12. 6.84×10^{-3}

13. 3.2×10^{-5}

14. 8.09×10^{-7}

15. 5.4×10^{-1}

16. 8.004×10^{-3}

17. $3.054\ 7 \times 10^{-1}$

18. 6.09×10^{2}

19. 4.68×10^{7}

20. 1.909×10^{-5}

Exercise 4.14

1. 4×10^{10}, 40 000 000 000

2. $3.155\ 76 \times 10^{9}$, 3 155 760 000 sec (allowing for leap years 365.25 days)

3. 3.6×10^{10}, 36 000 000 000

4. 4.8×10^{7}, 48 000 000

5. 1.5×10^{-7}, 0.000 000 15

6. $3.142\ 8571 \times 10^{6}$, £3 142 857.10

7. $1.666\ 66 \times 10^{9}$, 1 666 666 667, £1.67×10^{8}, £166 666 667

8. 3×10^{4} mm, 1.8×10^{4} mm, 1.36×10^{11} mg,
30 000 mm, 18 000 mm, 136 000 000 000 mg

9. 2.2×10^{4} mm/sec, 22 222 mm/sec

10. 1136×10^{6} mm /60^{2}, 315 555.56 mm/sec

11. 1.5×10^{3}, 1500

12. $2^{10} \times 2^{10} \times 4 \times 8$, 33 554 432, $3.355\ 4432 \times 10^{7}$

13. (a) $300\ 000 \times 60 \times 60 \times 24 \times 365 = 9.5 \times 10^{12}$ kilometres .
(b) 4.07×10^{13}, 40 700 000 000 000

14. 3.07×10^{13}, 30 700 000 000 000

15. 4.5×10^{9}, 4 500 000 000

Exercise 4.15: Extension questions 1

1. 3

2. 7

3. 8

4. 2

5. 27

6. 49

7. 7

8. 25

9. 11

10. 5

11. 9

12. 27

Exercise 4.16: Extension questions 2

1. ±1

2. ±3

3. ±4

4. ±9

5. ±11

6. ±17

7. ±16

8. ±12

9. ±19

10. ±25

11. ±18

12. ±15

Exercise 4.17: Extension questions 3

1. 12
2. 16
3. $\sqrt{3} \times \sqrt{7}$
4. 6

5. $2\sqrt{2}$
6. $5\sqrt{5}$
7. 18
8. 14

9. $\sqrt{3} \times \sqrt{18}$ or $3\sqrt{6}$
10. 12
11. 9
12. 18

13. $5\sqrt{3}$
14. $3\sqrt{3}$
15. $9\sqrt{2}$
16. $6\sqrt{2}$
17. $2\sqrt{15}$
18. 8
19. 15

20. $4\sqrt{6}$
21. $7\sqrt{6}$
22. $6\sqrt{2}$
23. $8\sqrt{3}$
24. $6\sqrt{5}$
25. 12
26. $6\sqrt{15}$

Exercise 4.18: Extension questions 4

Other correct answers are acceptable.

1. 60
2. 18
3. 30
4. $5(\sqrt{8} + \sqrt{3})$ or $10\sqrt{2} + 5\sqrt{3}$
5. $5\sqrt{20}$
6. $\dfrac{4\sqrt{3}}{3}$

7. $\dfrac{\sqrt{6}\left(\sqrt{3} + \sqrt{2}\right)}{12}$ or $\dfrac{3\sqrt{2} + 2\sqrt{3}}{12}$
8. $\dfrac{6\sqrt{5}}{5}$
9. 0
10. $\dfrac{\sqrt{2}}{2}$
11. $\dfrac{5\sqrt{6}}{6}$
12. $2\sqrt{2}$

Exercise 4.19: Summary exercise

1. (a) 3^3 (b) 2^6 (c) 4^5 (d) 7^3
2. (a) 27   (b) 64   (c) 1024   (d) 343
3. (a) 2^3 (b) 5^3 (c) 2^7 (d) 3^4 or 9^2

4.   (a) $\dfrac{1}{4}$ (b) $\dfrac{1}{243}$ (c) $\dfrac{1}{343}$

5.   (a) 3^6 (g) 5^{10}
     (b) 7^3 (h) 5^3
     (c) 3^{-3} (i) 2^{-6}
     (d) 2×3^3 (j) $3^3 + 2^3$
     (e) $5^2 \div 3^3$ (k) $6^4 \div 2^4$ or 3^4
     (f) $3^3 \times 5^2$ (l) $5^3 - 4^2$

6.   (a) 4^{-1} (d) 2^2
     (b) 3^1 or 3   (e) 5^{-4}
     (c) 4^{-4} (f) 7^0 or 1

7.   (a) $x = \pm 4$ (b) $a = \pm 10$ (c) $b = \pm\dfrac{1}{2}$

8.   (a) ± 4 (b) 1.21   (c) 0.09   (d) ± 0.2
9.   (a) 70 000   (b) 2 750 000   (c) 0.000 15   (d) 0.009 702
10. (a) 4.7×10^4 (b) 8.1×10^{-3} (c) 5.06×10^8 (d) 4.02×10^{-4}
11. 6 200 000 000, 6.2×10^9
12. (a) 5   (b) 3   (c) 12   (d) 70

End of chapter 4 activity: Chain letters

1.   3125

2.   46 656

3.   100 000

4.   If x is the number of letters and y is the number on the list then the total is:
     x^y

5. 1×10^{10}, 10 000 000 000 (ten thousand million)
     Population of Britain is approx 60 000 000 (60 million)

Chapter 5: Percentages

This chapter revises the basic principles of percentages before moving on to percentage increases and decreases, finding the original amount and compound interest. Although the use of a calculator is essential for the majority of the chapter, it is important to ensure that pupils are recording their working out in the correct manner.

A good rule to follow is:
Write down the calculation you are going to do before touching the buttons.

Exercise 5.1

1. (i) (a) 20%   (b) 30%   (c) 62.5%   (d) 16%
    (ii) (a) 0.2   (b) 0.3   (c) 0.625   (d) 0.16

2. (i) (a) 0.14   (b) 0.65   (c) 0.33   (d) 0.44

    (ii) (a) $\frac{7}{50}$ (b) $\frac{13}{20}$ (c) $\frac{33}{100}$ (d) $\frac{11}{25}$

3. (i) (a) $\frac{1}{8}$ (b) $\frac{2}{3}$ (c) $\frac{1}{6}$ (d) $\frac{3}{8}$

    (ii) (a) 0.125   (b) $0.\dot{6}$ (c) $0.1\dot{6}$ (d) 0.375

4. (i) (a) $\frac{1}{3}$ (b) $\frac{5}{6}$ (c) $\frac{2}{9}$

    (ii) (a) $33\frac{1}{3}\%$ (b) $83\frac{1}{3}\%$ (c) $22\frac{2}{9}\%$

5. 12%
6. 36%
7. £3.50
8. 1.8 m
9. 30 minutes
10. £1.75
11. 315 km
12. 44%
13. 42p
14. (a) £22   (b) £30.80   (c) £35.20
15. 60%
16. £5.75
17. £625
18. £26.25
19. £1.70

20. $66\frac{2}{3}\%$

21. £3.75
22. 6 boxes. £11.40
23. (a) 25%   (b) $33\frac{1}{3}$%   (c) $41\frac{2}{3}$%
24. (a) 20%
   (b) Pie chart sections should be as follows:
     car 144°
     walk 60°
     bus 84°
     public transport 72°

Exercise 5.2

A calculator can be used for this exercise.

1.   (a) Teddy Bear   £2.10
    (b) Fax machine   £48.83
    (c) Tennis Racquet   £8.58
    (d) Bicycle   £26.25
    (e) Baseball Cap   £0.44
    (f) Football   £2.80

2.   (a) Teddy Bear   £14.10
    (b) Fax machine   £327.83
    (c) Tennis Racquet   £57.58
    (d) Bicycle   £176.25
    (e) Baseball Cap   £2.94
    (f) Football   £18.80

3.   (a) Kite   £2.25
    (b) Beach ball   60p
    (c) Walkman   £5.25
    (d) Alarm clock   £1.80
    (e) Stereo system   £22.50
    (f) Kettle   £3.75

4.   (a) Kite   £12.75
    (b) Beach ball   £3.40
    (c) Walkman   £29.75
    (d) Alarm clock   £10.20
    (e) Stereo system   £127.50
    (f) Kettle   £21.25

5. £4.80
6. 20%
7. 4 balls for £3.60 gives 9% discount
8. 14

Exercise 5.3

1. Various answers may be given. Possible answers are as follows:
    (a) The highest amount is £523.27
        The route to the highest amount is D C F G K O
    (b) The lowest amount is £61.24
        The route to the lowest amount is A F E I J M
    (c) The route to £500 is C F G K O (to £502.34)

2. As last exercise q.2
Teddy Bear	£14.10
Fax machine	£327.83
Tennis Racquet	£57.58
Bicycle	£176.25
Baseball Cap	£2.94
Football	£18.80

3. As last exercise q.4
Kite	£12.75
Beach ball	£3.40
Walkman	£29.75
Alarm clock	£10.20
Stereo system	£127.50
Kettle	£21.25

4. (a) 1.04 (b) 1.05 (c) 0.92 (d) 0.8 (e)0.82 (f) 0.85
    (g) 0.92 if you are paying commission then you receive the sale price less commission, but if you are buying then you pay the hammer price plus commission.
    (h) 1.125 (i) 1.1 (j) 0.84 (k) 0.68
    (l) 0.6 (you receive 0.6 (60%) of earnings)

5. £43.12
6. £28
7. £14.85
8. £147 000
9. £7225, £6502.50
10. 24.4 m
11. 136 min or 2 hours 16 minutes
12. 4160 cm^3

Exercise 5.4

The tax stated here is not exactly that set for 2004 – 5 but near enough for the purposes of the exercise. You may wish to set this exercise up as an Excel spreadsheet. The answers are given in table form as it is a sensible way of working out tax.

1.

	Salary	Taxable	10% of 2000	22% of next 28 000	40% of rest	Take home
a)	12 000	7300	200	1166		10 634
b)	20 000	15 300	200	2926		16 874
c)	15 000	10 300	200	1826		12 974
d)	50 000	45 300	200	6600	6120	37 080

(a) £10 634
(b) £16 874
(c) £12 974
(d) £37 520

2.

	Salary	Taxable	10% of 2000	22% of next 28 000	40% of rest	Take home
a)	16 000	11 300	200	2046		13 754
	15 000	10 300	200	1826		12 974
b)	32 000	27 300	200	5566		26 234
	26 000	21 300	200	4246		21 554
c)	28 000	23 300	200	4686		23 114
	10 000	5300	200	726		9074
d)	120 000	115 300	200	6160	34 120	79 520
	5000	300	30			4970

(a) The couple earned £26 728
(b) The couple earned £47 788
(c) The couple earned £32 188
(d) The couple earned £84 490

3. The singer paid the smallest percentage of tax and the model the highest.

Exercise 5.5

1.	Original value: £15	New value: £12	decrease
2.	Original value: £52.50	New value: £67.86	increase
3.	Original value: £2500	New value: £1750	decrease
4.	Original value: 416	New value: 395	decrease
5.	Original value: £300	New value: £423	increase
6.	Original value: £18 000	New value: £14 400	decrease
7.	Original value: £50	New value: £160	increase
8.	Original value: £220	New value: £190	decrease
9.	Original value: £15	New value: £12	decrease

10. 1. Decrease 20%
2. Increase 29%
3. Decrease 30%
4. Decrease 5%
5. Increase 41%

6. Decrease 20%
7. Increase 220%
8. Decrease 14%
9. Decrease 20%

Exercise 5.6

1. £2200
2. £50
3. 160 000
4. 25 000
5. £12

6. 2.4 litres
7. 152 cm
8. 154
9. £2.40
10. £6800, £8000

Exercise 5.7

1. Original £375
2. New £3400
3. New £22 500
4. Original £1500
5. Original £42
6. New 63
7. Original 11p
8. Original 14 545 cm^3 or 14 litres (correct rounding to 2 d.p. gives you 15 litres, but then the 10% extra will bring you over 16, therefore the answer has to be rounded down)
9. Jan 96 New £251.86
Jan 94 Original £220
10. Price before VAT £400, old selling price £460, new selling price £470

The next two questions lead into compound interest.

11. (a) New £213.29
(b) New £271.96 The important thing here is that you cannot multiply your previous answer by 1.02

Exercise 5.8: Extension questions – Compound interest

Once the pupils have grasped the concept of compound interest this is a good exercise to use to show how spreadsheets can be used (especially q.4).

1. (a) £73.47
(b) £107.95
(c) £199.80
(d) £251.69
2. (a) £5600
(b) £7024.64
(c) £8811.71
3. (a) £9292.80
(d) £1440
(b) £6332.78
(e) £455.73
(c) £3342.01
4. (a) £25 525.63
(b) 15
(c) yes
(d) £110 000 (rounded)

5.   (a) 8 years
      (b) 35 years
6.   In ten years time (after sensible rounding)
      (a) £10 590
      (b) £570
      (c) £16
      Ten years ago
      (a) £3890
      (b) £210
      (c) £6
7.   (a) 4 and a half years
      (b) 8 and a half years
      (c) 6 years
      (d) The answers do not depend on the original price of the goods at all because they are multiplied by $(1.05)^x$, (a) is when $(1.05)^x = 1.25$, (b) is when $(1.05)^x = 1.5$ and (c) is when $(1.05)^x = 1.33$

Exercise 5.9: Summary exercise

1.   79%
2.   1 hour and 52.5 minutes
3.   271 kg
4.   4.8%
5.   (a) £131.25
      (b) £15.73
6.   (a) £472.50
      (b) £12.50
      (c) £148.93
7.   £20
8.   £387 000
9.   16 minutes
10.   £2120

End of chapter 5 activity: The trading game

Practical

Chapter 6: Equations and inequations

Exercise 6.1

1.	8	**6.**	-24	**11.**	$\frac{2}{3}$	**16.**	$1\frac{2}{9}$
2.	7	**7.**	$7\frac{1}{2}$	**12.**	-1	**17.**	14
3.	$1\frac{2}{3}$	**8.**	-4	**13.**	-14	**18.**	7
4.	32	**9.**	1	**14.**	-7	**19.**	$8\frac{2}{3}$
5.	$1\frac{1}{5}$	**10.**	-2	**15.**	0	**20.**	$-5\frac{1}{3}$

Exercise 6.2

1. (a) $x - 10$ (b) $x + 4$ (c) $x - 5$ (d) $x + 9$ (e) $x - 1$ (f) $x - 1$
2. $2(x - 1) = x + 9$ My age $x = 11$
3. (a) $4x$ (b) $x + 6$ (c) $4x + 6$
4. $3(x + 6) = 4x + 6$ My father is 48
5. (a) $x + 2$
   (b) $4(x + 2)$
   (c) $4(x + 2) = 5x$ I am 8
6. (a) (i) $3x$ (ii) $4x$
   (b) $4x - 9 = 3x$ or $3x + 9 = 4x$ I am 9
7. (a) (i) $x - 4$ (ii) $x - 4$ (iii) $x - 8$
   (b) $x - 4 = 2(x - 8)$ He is 8
8. 12
9. 16
10. 12

Exercise 6.3

1. (a) (i) $x + 4$
      (ii) $2(x + 4)$
   (b) $3(x + 4) = 4x$, $x = 12$
   (c) 32 ducklings

2. (a) (i) Red marbles $4x$
      (ii) Green marbles $12x$
   (b) $17x = 34$ Yellow marbles $x = 2$

3. (a) (i) $x - 3$ (ii) $2x$
   (b) $4x - 3 = 21$, $x = 6$, my sister picked 3 kg

4.   (a) (i) $x + 4$ (ii) $100x$ (iii) $200(x + 4)$
     (b) $100x + 200(x + 4) = 2300$ Profit on each widget and wotsit 5p and 9p

5.   (a) $1.1x = 35.2$ $x = 32$ cm
     (b) $1.2x = 6$ $x = £5$
     (c) $x \div 1.1 = 15$ $x = £16.50$
     (d) $x \div 1.25 = 4$ $x = 5$ kg

6. $x + x + 5 = 195$ $x = 95$, so there are 95 girls and 100 boys

7. $8 + 4x + x + 1 + 3 = 24$ 2 hours 24 min

8. $5x - (15 + 0.75x) = 250$ 63 cars

9. $5 + 3x = 2 + 8x$ The mass of one measure of chemical A is 0.6 mg

10. $18x + 100 = 20(x - 10)$ The average height of my class is 150 cm

Equations with Fractions

Many pupils find equations with fractions very off putting, possibly fearing that they are going to get into tangled fraction arithmetic. Some initial examples showing how to get rid of all the fractions in one simple multiplication, even before you start these exercises, can help to reassure the pupils that these equations are not so difficult.

Do remind pupils to check their answers by substituting back into the equations. With fractional answers this can become quite difficult and the correct use of a calculator should be encouraged.

Exercise 6.4

1.   12

2.   12

3.   10

4.   8

5.   10

6. $6\frac{1}{2}$

7. $-5\frac{1}{3}$

8. $\frac{1}{2}$

9. $\frac{2}{5}$

10. -2

Exercise 6.5

1. 9
2. 20
3. 6
4. $-3\frac{1}{2}$
5. -2
6. $3\frac{1}{3}$
7. -6
8. $1\frac{5}{7}$

9. $-2\frac{1}{2}$
10. $1\frac{7}{13}$
11. $-3\frac{1}{3}$
12. $1\frac{11}{12}$
13. $-1\frac{1}{2}$
14. $\frac{1}{21}$
15. $-1\frac{3}{4}$
16. $1\frac{5}{11}$

Exercise 6.6

1. $\frac{3}{8}$
2. $\frac{8}{15}$
3. $\frac{14}{15}$

4. $1\frac{1}{9}$
5. $1\frac{11}{16}$
6. $2\frac{1}{2}$

This next set are usually found only on scholarship papers, but are still good recreation for your more able pupils.

7. 24
8. $-7\frac{1}{5}$
9. $3\frac{5}{9}$
10. $8\frac{4}{5}$

11. $-\frac{4}{21}$
12. $-6\frac{2}{3}$
13. $\frac{15}{44}$
14. $\frac{5}{69}$

Exercise 6.7

1. 3, 4, 5

6. −6, −7

2. 1, 2, 3, 4

7. 0, 1, 2, 3

3. 6, 7, 8

8. −1, 0, 1, 2

4. 1, 2, 3, 4

9. 4, 5, 6, 7

5. −2, −1, 0, 1, 2

10. 5, 6, 7, 8, 9

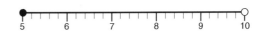

Exercise 6.8

1. $x < 2$
2. $x \geq 3$
3. $x \geq 3$

4. $x > 28$
5. $x \leq 7$
6. $x < 2$

7. $x < 1$

11. $x \leq 27$

8. $x > \dfrac{2}{3}$

12. $x > 0$

9. $x \geq 1$
10. $x > 11$

13. $x \leq 24$
14. $x \geq 10$

At this stage of equation solving, it is worth emphasising that it is better to keep the x term positive. This is particularly true when solving inequalities. By keeping the x term positive we do not have to worry about reversing the inequality.

Exercise 6.9

1. $x < \dfrac{1}{2}$

2. $x > -\dfrac{1}{2}$

3. $x \geq -\dfrac{4}{5}$

4. $x < 2\dfrac{2}{3}$

5. $x \geq -36$

6. $x > 6\dfrac{2}{3}$

7. $x \geq 1$

8. $x > 28$

9. $x \leq 9$

10. $x < 2$

11. $x \leq -4\dfrac{1}{2}$

12. $x > 6\dfrac{2}{3}$

13. $x < 1\dfrac{1}{4}$

14. $x > 3$

15. $x \geq -1$

16. $x \geq 2\dfrac{6}{13}$

Exercise 6.10: Extension questions

The later questions in this exercise are strictly for scholars, but you may see questions like 1 to 5 in old Common Entrance papers.

1. (a) $-3 < x < -\dfrac{1}{2}$

    $x = -2, -1$

    (b) $1 \leq x < 3$

    $x = 1, 2$

    (c) $10 \leq x < 14$

    $x = 10, 11, 12, 13$

    (d) $1\dfrac{1}{2} < x \leq 8\dfrac{1}{4}$

    $x = 2, 3, 4, 5, 6, 7, 8$

2. (a) 1 (0 is not normally regarded as a perfect square)
    (b) 2

3. (a) 25
    (b) 10
    (c) 18
    (d) 13 or 23

4. (a) $x < 3\dfrac{1}{2}$

    (b) 2 and 3

5. (a) $x < -2$
    (b) -3

6. (a) $x \leq 5$
    (b) 5

7. (a) $1 < x < 1\frac{5}{7}$

    (b) There are none.

8. $3 \le x < 3\frac{1}{3}$, 3

9. $7\frac{1}{5} < x \le 9$ 8 and 9

10. Because $x < 13\frac{1}{2}$ and $x > 14\frac{1}{4}$

11. (a) (i) True, 2 is greater than $1\frac{1}{2}$ (iv) False, 3 is not greater than $3\frac{1}{2}$

        (ii) False, they are equal   (v) True, 101 is greater than 100

        (iii) True, 19 is greater than 5   (vi) False, 3 is not greater than $4\frac{1}{2}$

    (b) (iv) $x \, \Delta \, 2x - 1$ is always true.
    (c) (i) $x \, \Delta \, x + 1$ is true when $x > 1$
        (vi) $x \, \Delta \, x^2$ is true when $x < 2$

12. (a) (i) True, 4 is less than $3\frac{1}{2}$ plus 1

        (ii) True, 3 is less than $2\frac{1}{2}$ plus 1

        (iii) False, 7 is not less than $5\frac{1}{2}$ plus 1 7 Δ 11

        (iv) False, 50 is not less than $25\frac{1}{2}$ plus 1

        (v) False, 101 equals 100 plus 1

        (vi) True, 5 is less than $12\frac{1}{2}$ plus 1

    (b) (ii) always true $x \, ¥ \, 2x$ (iii) $x \, ¥ \, 2x + 1$, (iv) $x \, ¥ \, 2x - 1$, (v) $x \, ¥ \, 2(x + 1)$ and
        (vi) $x \, ¥ \, x^2$ are always true
    (c) (i) $x \, ¥ \, x + 1$ is true when $x < 2$

Exercise 6.11: Summary exercise

1. (a) 1   (d) $\frac{1}{2}$

    (b) $1\frac{1}{2}$ (e) 5

    (c) $1\frac{2}{3}$ (f) $-3\frac{1}{3}$

2. (a) $3x$
(b) $x - 4$
(c) $3x - 4$
(d) $3x - 4 = 4(x - 4)$ $x = 12$

3. (a) $5x + 8$
(b) $4x + 12$
(c) $4x + 12 = 5x + 8$, $x = 4$

4. (a) -9 (d) $2\frac{1}{2}$

(b) $4\frac{1}{2}$ (e) $6\frac{2}{3}$

(c) $2\frac{2}{3}$ (f) $5\frac{5}{8}$

5. (a) $x = 1, 2, 3, 4$ (b) $x = -2, -1, 0, 1$

6. (a) $x < 4$ (b) $x \geq 2\frac{1}{2}$ (c) $x \leq \frac{5}{6}$

7. $\frac{3}{5} < x < 2\frac{2}{5}$, $x = 1, 2$

End of chapter 6 activity: Polyhedral numbers

1. You are adding triangle numbers.

2.

n		tetra no:
1	1	1
2	1 + 3	4
3	1 + 3 + 6	10
4	1 + 3 + 6 + 10	20
5	1 + 3 + 6 + 10 + 15	35
6	1 + 3 + 6 + 10 + 15 + 21	56
7	1 + 3 + 6 + 10 + 15 + 21 + 28	84
8	1 + 3 + 6 + 10 + 15 + 21 + 28 + 36	120
9	1 + 3 + 6 + 10 + 15 + 21 + 28 + 36 + 45	165
10	1 + 3 + 6 + 10 + 15 + 21 + 28 + 36 + 45 + 55	220
11	1 + 3 + 6 + 10 + 15 + 21 + 28 + 36 + 45 + 55 + 66	286

3.   (a) 10th is 220
(b) 100th is 171 700

4. nth tetrahedral number is $\dfrac{n(n+1)(n+2)}{6}$

5.   The next set of polyhedral numbers is one formed by square based pyramids. The 1st such number will be 1, the second will be $1 + 4 = 5$, the third $1 + 4 + 9 \ldots$ etc.

n		Square based pyramid no:
1	1	1
2	1 + 4	5
3	1 + 4 + 9	14
4	1 + 4 + 9 + 16	30
5	1 + 4 + 9 + 16 + 25	55
6	1 + 4 + 9 + 16 + 25 + 36	91
7	1 + 4 + 9 + 16 + 25 + 36 + 49	140
8	1 + 4 + 9 + 16 + 25 + 36 + 49 + 64	204

10th is 385
100th is 338 350

nth square based pyramid number is $\dfrac{n(n+1)(2n+1)}{6}$

n		Pentagon based pyramid no:
1	1	1
2	1 + 5	6
3	1 + 5 + 12	18
4	1 + 5 + 12 + 22	40
5	1 + 5 + 12 + 22 + 35	75
6	1 + 5 + 12 + 22 + 35 + 51	126
7	1 + 5 + 12 + 22 + 35 + 51 + 70	196
8	1 + 5 + 12 + 22 + 35 + 51 + 70 + 92	288

10th is 550
100th is 505 000

nth pentagon based pyramid number is $\dfrac{n^2(n+1)}{2}$

If you compare your sequences to Pascal's triangle you will see that the tetrahedral numbers form the diagonal under the triangle numbers, which is very satisfactory.

It would be good if the other polyhedral numbers were found here too but they are not. The diagonals in fact form a continuation of the pattern for the tetrahedral numbers:

$$\frac{(n+1)(n+2)(n+3)n+4)}{2 \times 3 \times 4}$$

A good extension to this activity would be to see if you can find a 3-dimensional sequence which would give the numerical sequence.

Chapter 7: Indices and algebra

Exercise 7.1

1. x^7
2. b^6
3. a^7
4. 2^9
5. 2^{a+b}

6. 3^5
7. a^9
8. 3^{a+b}
9. x^6
10. 3^6

11. x^6
12. b^7
13. a^8
14. 2^{x+y+1}
15. a^{x+y}

16. $2^a \times 3^b$
17. a^{2y+2}
18. xy^a
19. x^{x+y+1}
20. $(ab^2)^y$

Exercise 7.2

1. a
2. b^4
3. x^3
4. 2^3
5. 3^{x-y}
6. a

7. x^4

8. $5^0 = 1$
9. x^5
10. $a^0 = 1$
11. $4y^4$
12. x^{x-1}
13. $2x^{a-3}$

14. $\dfrac{a^{b-c}}{2}$

Exercise 7.3

1. 2^{-3}

2. a^{-3}

3. x^{-3}

4. $x^0 = 1$

5. 7^{a-b}

6. x^{-1}

7. b^{-4}

8. $a^0 = 1$

9. x^2

10. $a^2 \div b^2$ or $\left(\dfrac{a}{b}\right)^2$

11. $2x^{-1}$

12. $\dfrac{1}{5a^3}$

13. $\dfrac{y^3}{3}$

14. $\dfrac{1}{4x^3}$

Exercise 7.4

Although this exercise goes beyond the Common Entrance syllabus, it promotes better understanding of index numbers

1. 3^8
2. 2^6
3. x^6
4. a^{15}
5. $4b^6$

6. $243a^{15}$
7. 4^{ab}
8. x^{m^2}
9. $9a^{2m}$
10. $2^m x^{m^2}$

11. 3^{-2}
12. 4^8
13. 2^{-2}
14. $\dfrac{x^6}{27}$
15. a^4

16. $\dfrac{1}{27x^5}$
17. $8a^6$
18. 16
19. $\dfrac{a^5}{3}$
20. $\dfrac{1}{27}$

Index numbers as fractions

Again, this is not strictly on the syllabus but is useful work for your potential scholars.

Exercise 7.5

1. 3
2. 2
3. 5
4. 3
5. 4
6. 5

7. 2
8. x
9. $2x$
10. $3x$
11. x^2
12. $\dfrac{1}{2x}$

Exercise 7.6

1. a^6
2. $6a^6$
3. $3b + b^2 + 2b^3$
4. $6b^2$
5. $6a^4b^4$

6. $8x^2y$
7. $3xy + x^2y$
8. $4xy + x^2y - xy^2$
9. $12a^3b^2c^2$
10. $2bc + a^2b + 4ac$

Exercise 7.7

.	$3ab$	6.	$\dfrac{3a^2}{5}$	11.	$3xy$
.	$3a^2$	7.	$\dfrac{a^2}{8b^2}$	12.	$\dfrac{3a^2}{b}$
.	$3a^2$	8.	$\dfrac{1}{4m}$	13.	$\dfrac{3}{2x}$
.	$4y$	9.	$\dfrac{8y^2}{5x}$	14.	$\dfrac{3ac^2}{2b}$
.	5	10.	$\dfrac{2b^4}{3c}$	15.	$\dfrac{3xy}{2z}$

Exercise 7.8

.	$2x^2 + x$	7.	$x^3 + x^2 - x$
2.	$3x^2 - x$	8.	$4x^2 - 3x^3$
3.	$4x - 3x^2$	9.	$6x^3 - 4x^2$
4.	$2x^2 + 8x$	10.	$2x^4 + 3x^3 + 4x^2$
5.	$6x^2 - 15x$	11.	$x^5 + x^3$
6.	$x^3 + x^2$	12.	$6x^5 - 12x^4 + 9x^3$

13.	$4x^2 - 5x$	18.	$4x^2 - 3x$
14.	$x^2 + 8x$	19.	$9x^2 - 11x$
15.	$2x^2 + 2x$	20.	$-x^2 - 7x$
16.	$-3x^2$	21.	$7x^2 - 2x$
17.	$4x^2 - 13x$	22.	$-12x$

This last set of questions is good for those scholars who are going to have to deal with expanding brackets such as $(x - y)(x + y)$

23.	$x^2 + 2xy + y^2$	28.	$5x^2y^2 + 2xy^2 - 4x^2y$
24.	$6x^2 - 4y^2$	29.	$-4x^2 - 5x^2y$
25.	$2x^2 + 2xy + 2y^2$	30.	$3xy^2 - 6x^2y - x^2y^2$
26.	$-x^2y$	31.	$6x^4 - 15x^3y + 3x^3 - 8y$
27.	$5x^2 + 5xy$	32.	$6x^3y + 2x^2y^2 - 9xy^3$

Exercise 7.9

1.	$3(x + 2)$	4.	$2(9 - 2y)$
2.	$4(2y - 1)$	5.	$8(3x + 2)$
3.	$3(2 + 3x)$	6.	$7x - 6$ Does not factorise.

7.	$x(x + 5)$	10.	$5x - y^2$ Does not factorise.
8.	$y(y - 7)$	11.	$x(x^2 + 2)$
9.	$x(3 + x)$	12.	$x^2(x - 3)$

13. $2x(x + 2)$
14. $3a(2 - 3a)$
15. $3y(3x + 2y - 1)$

16. $9a^2 - 8b$ Does not factorise.
17. $3x(4x - 3y + 2)$
18. $4a(2b - a)$

19. $x(3y + 16x + 4)$
20. $2ab(4a + 7)$
21. $8x^2 + 5y^2$ Does not factorise.
22. $3(4y^2 - 3y + x)$
23. $4y(3 + 2x^2 - 4y)$
24. $3a^2 + 6b^2 - 2ab$ Does not factorise.
25. $4xy(3 + 4x - y)$

26. $14x^2 + 8xy + 3y^2$ Does not factorise.
27. $2(5xy + 7y^2 - 2)$
28. $16x^2 - 12xy - 9$ Does not factorise.
29. $2x(8x - 7y - 3)$
30. $2b(10a^2 - 2ab - 1)$
31. $4ab(5a - b + 2)$
32. $2x(8y^2 + 4x - y)$

Trial and improvement

Students tend to read this as 'trial and error' but they should be encouraged to keep improving their answers. It is good practice to get into the routine of putting notes in the final column of the table. It will help pupils find the correct answer if they by keep a note of too small or too big as they go along.

There can often be confusion about how far they should keep on searching.
If the answer is to be given to 2 decimal places then they must work to 3 d.p.

Many pupils will assume that the closer answer is correct so it is worth putting the equations on a spreadsheet and graphing them, thus showing them that these are not linear relationships.

Exercise 7.10

1.   (a) (i) 6.7   (ii) 6.72
      (b) (i) 5.6   (ii) 5.64
      (c) (i) 9.8   (ii) 9.77

2.   (a) $h + 6$
      (b) $h(h + 6)$

(c)

Height	Length	Area	Note
8	14	112	too small
9	15	135	too big
8.2	14.2	116.44	too small
8.3	14.3	118.69	too big
8.25	14.25	117.56..	too small

The height lies between 8.3 and 8.25 and therefore equals 8.3 cm to one decimal place.

(a) $b(b - 5)$

(b)

b	$b - 5$	Area	Note
10	5	50	too big
9	4	36	too small
9.2	4.2	38.64	too small
9.3	4.3	39.99	too small
9.4	4.4	41.36	too big
9.31	4.31	40.126	too big
9.305	4.305	40.058 ...	too big

Height lies between 9.3 and 9.305 and therefore equals 9.30 to 2 decimal places.

Length 9.4 m, width 7.4 m
Height 8.25 cm
8.9 m
9.6 cm
9.6 m
(a) $(x + 5)$
(b) $(x + 5)^2 - x^2$
(c) 15.7 cm

0. (a) $Area = \dfrac{x(2x + 4)}{2} = x(x + 2)$

(b)

x	$x + 1$	$x + 3$	Area	Note
3	4	6	15	too small
4	5	7	24	too big
3.5	4.5	6.5	19.25	too small
3.6			20.16	too big
3.58			19.976	too small
3.59			20.068	too big
3.585			20.022	too big

x lies between 3.58 and 3.585 and therefore equals 3.58 to 2 decimal places.

Exercise 7.11: Extension questions – More about square roots

This method of working out square roots is very effective. Your more persistent students may wish to calculate y_3

1. $2\frac{5}{6} = 2.8\dot{3}$

2. $4\frac{1}{8} = 4.125$

3. $4\frac{4}{5} = 4.8$

4. $3\frac{7}{8} = 3.875$

5. $5\frac{1}{5} = 5.2$

6. $10\frac{1}{4} = 10.25$

7. $3\frac{5}{8} = 3.625$

8. $4\frac{7}{10} = 4.7$

9. $9\frac{2}{9} = 9.\dot{2}$

10. $4\frac{3}{5} = 4.6$

11. $7\frac{3}{7} = 7.43$

12. $8\frac{1}{2} = 8.5$

With a calculator:

1. 2.83
2. 4.12
3. 4.80
4. 3.87

5. 5.20
6. 10.25
7. 3.61
8. 4.69

9. 9.2̇2
10. 4.58
11. 7.42
12. 8.49

Exercise 7.12: Summary exercise

1. (a) a^5 (b) b^5 (c) c^3d^2
2. (a) a^2 (b) b^3 (c) c^3
3. (a) a^{-2} (b) b^0 (c) c^{-4}
4. (a) $a^6 + a^5$ (b) $4b^3$ (c) $c^4 + c + c^2$
5. (a) $\dfrac{ab^2}{2}$ (b) $\dfrac{5ab}{c}$ (c) $2a^2$

6. (a) $x^2 + 3x$ (b) $6x^2 - 10x$ (c) $6x^2 - x^3$
7. (a) $4x^2 + x$ (b) $10x^2 - 28x$
8. (a) $3(x + 3)$ (d) $3(x^2 - 4y)$ (g) $y(12x^2 + 5y - 8)$
   (b) $12x - 7$ (e) $3(x^2 - 4x + 1)$ (h) $3x^2(3x - 2y + 5)$
   (c) $2y(2x + y)$ (f) $2(2x^2y - 4y^2 + 3x)$

9. x lies between 11.700 and 11.705 and therefore equals 11.70 to 2 decimal places.

End of chapter 7 activity: My great uncle's bequest

The spreadsheet should come out like this:

Year	Scheme A	Total A	Scheme B	Total B	Scheme C	Total C	Scheme D	Total D
1	100	100	10	10	10.00	10.00	1	1
2	90	190	20	30	15.00	25.00	2	3
3	80	270	30	60	22.50	47.50	4	7
4	70	340	40	100	33.75	81.25	8	15
5	60	400	50	150	50.63	131.88	16	31
6	50	450	60	210	75.94	207.81	32	63
7	40	490	70	280	113.91	321.72	64	127
8	30	520	80	360	170.86	492.58	128	255
9	20	540	90	450	256.29	748.87	256	511
10	10	550	100	550	384.43	1133.30	512	1023

The answer really depends on how long you think Great Uncle Ben will live. Some pupils may investigate for more years, as you can see scheme D is rapidly overtaking scheme C.

The chart should look like this:

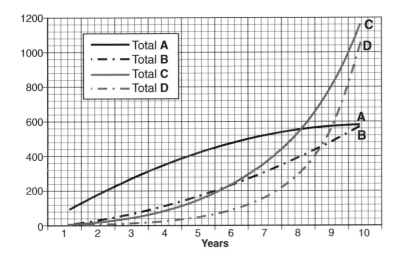

The Great Nephew's dilemma is to estimate how long Uncle Ben will live for. Scheme B is the safe option if he is not going to last more than 8 years. However if he is hale and hearty then scheme D will pay off best in 11 years and even more so in every year after that.

Chapter 8: Sequences

Exercise 8.1

1.	11, 13, 15,	rule is add 2
2.	36, 49, 64,	rule is add increasing odd numbers
3.	18, 21, 24,	rule is add 3
4.	21, 28, 36,	rule is add increasing numbers
5.	16, 19, 22,	rule is add 3
6.	35, 48, 63,	rule is add increasing odd numbers
7.	21, 34, 55,	rule is add the last two terms
8.	16, 22, 29,	rule is add increasing numbers
9.	22, 26, 30,	rule is add 4
10.	26, 31, 36,	rule is add 5

Exercise 8.2

1.   (a) 1. 1, 3, 5, 7, 9, ...   (i)   a table based sequence
          2. 1, 4, 9, 16, 25, ...   (ii) a square number type sequence
          3. 3, 6, 9, 12, 15, ...   (i)   a table based sequence
          4. 1, 3, 6, 10, 15, ...   (iii) a triangle number type sequence
          5. 1, 4, 7, 10, 13, ...   (i)   a table based sequence
          6. 0, 3, 8, 15, 24, ...   (ii) a square number type sequence
          7. 1, 1, 2, 3, 5, 8, 13, ... (iv) a Fibonnaci style sequence
          8. 1, 2, 4, 7, 11, ...   (iii) a triangle number type sequence
          9. 2, 6, 10, 14, 18, ...   (i)   a table based sequence
          10. 1, 6, 11, 16, 21, ...   (i)   a table based sequence

    (b) 1. $2n - 1$

        2. n^2

        3. $3n$

        4. $\frac{1}{2}n(n + 1)$

        5. $3n - 2$

        6. $n^2 - 1$

        7. (iv) A Fibonacci style sequence

        8. $\frac{1}{2}n(n - 1) + 1$

        9. $4n - 2$

        10. $5n - 4$

2.   (a) 17, 20, 23 $3n - 1$
          (b) 37, 50, 65 $n^2 + 1$

          (c) 29, 37, 46 $\frac{1}{2}n(n + 1) + 1$

          (d) 32, 37, 42 $5n - 3$

3. (a) −30, −35, −40   −5n
    (b) −18, −21, −24   −3n
    (c) −42, −49, −56   −7n
    (d) −24, −28, −32   −4n

4. (a) 5, 0, −5   35 − 5n
    (b) −6, −9, −12   12 − 3n
    (c) 65, 58, 51   107 − 7n
    (d) 0, −4, −8   24 − 4n

5. (a) −3, −6, −9   18 − 3n
    (b) 33, 22, 11   110 − 11n
    (c) 41, 39, 37   53 − 2n
    (d) −7, −10, −13   8 − 3n

Exercise 8.3

1. (a) 32, 64, 128
    (b) 0.5, 0.25, 0.125 or $\dfrac{1}{2}, \dfrac{1}{4}, \dfrac{1}{8}$

    (c) 0.0625, 0.03125, 0.015625
    (d) 0.01, 0.001, 0.0001
    (e) 0.04, 0.008, 0.0016

2. (a) (i) 125, 216, 343
        (ii) 625, 1296, 2401
    (b) (i) n^3 (ii) n^4

3. (a) 13, 17, 19 prime numbers
    (b) F, S, S days of the week
    (c) A, S, O months
    (d) S, S, E numbers

4. (a) 5, 4, 6
    (b) 7, 4, 9
    (c) 7, 2, 9
    (d) 16, 9, 32

5. (a) 5, 8, **11**, 14, 17, **20**
    (b) 0, 3, **8**, 15, **24**, 35
    (c) 4, **2**, 1, 0.5, **0.25**
    (d) 2, 3, 5, **6,** 8, 9, **11**
    (e) 2, 5, **7**, 12, **19**, 31

Exercise 8.4

1.   (a) 3   (b) 10   (c) 17   (d) 11
2.   (a) $S_2 = 3$ (b) $V_3 = 11$ (c) $U_5 = 17$ (d) $T_4 = 10$
3.   (a) $S_7 = 13$ (b) $T_9 = 25$ (c) $U_7 = 25$ (d) $V_8 = 36$
4.   (a) $S_6 = 11$, $S_7 = 13$, $S_8 = 15$
     (b) $T_6 = 16$, $T_7 = 19$, $T_8 = 22$
     (c) $U_6 = 21$, $U_7 = 25$, $U_8 = 29$
     (d) $V_6 = 26$, $V_7 = 31$, $V_8 = 36$
5.   (a) None of them (b) $U_6 = 21$ (c) $T_8 = 22$ (d) $S_{12} = 23$
6.   (a) $T_{34} = 100$ (b) $S_{51} = 101$ and $U_{26} = 101$ (c) None of them.
     (d) $S_{52} = 103$ also $T_{35} = 103$
7.   (a) $T_n = 3n - 2$ (b) $U_n = 4n - 3$ (c) $V_n = 5n - 4$

Exercise 8.5

1.   (a) $S_1 = 3$ (b) $S_2 = 8$ (c) $S_5 = 23$ (d) $S_{10} = 48$ (e) $S_{21} = 103$
2.   (a) 9. 15, 21, 63   (b) $T_{17} = 105$
3.   (a) $V_1 = 17$ (b) $V_2 = 14$ (c) $V_3 = 11$ (d) $V_{10} = -10$ (e) $V_7 = -1$
4.   (a) $W_1 = 4$ (b) $W_5 = 28$ (c) $W_{10} = 103$ (d) $W_{20} = 403$ (e) $W_{15} = 228$
5.   (a) $S_1 = 2$ (b) $S_2 = 4$ (c) $S_3 = 8$ (d) $S_5 = 32$ (e) $S_7 = 128$
6.   If the nth term of a sequence is give by the rule $T_n = 100 - 2n^2$
     (a) $T_1 = 98$ (b) $T_2 = 92$ (c) $T_4 = 68$ (d) $T_{10} = -100$ (e) $T_8 = -28$
7.   (a) $U_1 = -1$ (b) $U_2 = 0$ (c) $U_5 = 15$ (d) $U_{10} = 80$ (e) $U_{12} = 120$
8.   (a) $W_1 = 0$ (b) $W_2 = 4$ (c) $W_5 = 28$ (d) $W_{10} = 108$ (e) $W_{14} = 208$

Exercise 8.6

1.   (a)
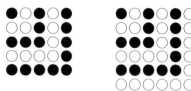

     (b) If you have x^2 then you add $2x + 1$ to get the next square. As x increases one by one you generate the sequence of odd numbers.

2.   (a)
 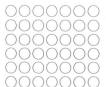

(b)

Rectangle number	Dots up	Dots along	Number of dots
R_1	1	2	$1 \times 2 = 2$
R_2	2	3	$2 \times 3 = 6$
R_3	3	4	$3 \times 4 = 12$
R_4	4	5	$4 \times 5 = 20$
R_5	5	6	$5 \times 6 = 30$
R_6	6	7	$6 \times 7 = 42$
R_n	n	$n + 1$	$n(n + 1)$

3. (a)

(b)

Triangle number	Number of dots
T_1	1
T_2	3
T_3	6
T_4	10
T_5	15
T_6	21

(c) Triangle numbers are half the rectangle numbers.

(d) $T_n = \frac{1}{2}n(n + 1)$

4. $n^2 - 1$

5. $n(n + 2)$

6. $\frac{1}{2}(n + 1)(n + 2) - 1$

7. $n(n + 1)$

Exercise 8.7

1. (a)

Pattern no:	White balls	Black balls	Total balls
1	1	0	1
2	2	2	4
3	5	4	9
4	8	8	16
5	13	12	25
6	18	18	36

(b) 100
(c) 50
(d) 50
(e) n^2
(f) If n is even there will be $\frac{1}{2}n^2$ black balls and white balls.

If n is odd there will be $\frac{1}{2}(n^2 + 1)$ white balls and $\frac{1}{2}(n^2 - 1)$ black balls.

2. (a)

Pattern no:	Black squares	White squares	Total squares
1	1	1	2
2	4	2	6
3	6	6	12
4	12	8	20
5	15	15	30
6	24	18	42

(b) 110
(c) 50
(d) 60
(e) If n is even there will be $\frac{1}{2}n^2$ white squares and $\frac{1}{2}n(n + 2)$ or $\frac{1}{2}n^2 + n$ black squares.

If n is odd there will be $\frac{1}{2}n(n + 1)$ black balls and $\frac{1}{2}n(n + 1)$ white balls.

(a)

Pattern no:	Black squares	White squares	Total squares
1	1	1	2
2	3	3	6
3	6	6	12
4	10	10	20
5	15	15	30
6	21	21	42

(b) 210 **(c)** 1275 **(d)** 10 100 **(e)** $\frac{1}{2}n(n+1)$

(a)

Pattern no:	Black balls	White balls	Total balls
1	1	0	1
2	2	1	3
3	4	2	6
4	6	4	10
5	9	6	15
6	12	9	21

(b) 55 **(c)** 25 **(d)** 30 **(e)** $\frac{1}{2}n(n+1)$

(f) If n is even there will be $\frac{1}{4}n^2$ black balls and $\frac{1}{4}n(n+2)$ white balls

If n is odd there will be $\frac{1}{4}(n+1)(n-1) = \frac{1}{4}n^2 - \frac{1}{4}$ black balls

and $\frac{1}{4}(n+1)^2 = \frac{1}{4}n^2 + \frac{1}{2}n + \frac{1}{4}$ white balls.

(a)

Pattern no:	Lines	Triangles
1	3	1
2	9	4
3	18	9
4	30	16
5	45	25
6	63	36

(b) 165 **(c)** 100 **(d)** 15150 **(e)** $\frac{3}{2}n(n+1)$ **(f)** n^2

Geometric sequences: An introduction to fractals

Fractals are fascinating but the mathematics behind them very quickly runs into very complicated sequences. The few we have chosen to examine here are accessible to pupils at this level. They give a clear example of the geometric design which leads to a numerical sequence that in turn can be described by an algebraic rule. Those pupils who are not inspired by algebra frequently enjoy the progression of the patterns.

Exercise 8.8

1. Perimeter is 27; area is 81

2. (a)   (b) Perimeter is 36 units; area is 108

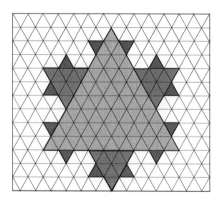

3. (a)   (b) Area is 120
                                          (c) Perimeter is 48

4.

Generation number	Area	No. of sides	Length of each side	Perimeter
1	81	3	9	27
2	108	12	3	36
3	120	48	1	48
4	$125\frac{1}{3}$	192	$\frac{1}{3}$	64

5.

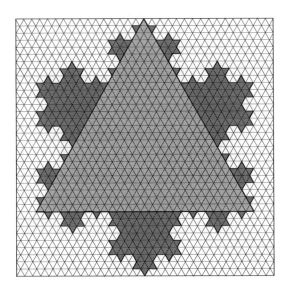

6. $3 \times 4^{n-1}$

7. $3 \times 4^{n-1} \times 3^{3-n} = 4^{n-1} \times 3^{4-n}$

8. Whilst the area is increasing by a smaller and smaller amount and will eventually become constant, the perimeter is increasing steadily.

Geometric sequences and numbers – Sierpinski's gasket

The generation of a pattern using a purely geometric sequence and then matching it to a pattern produced by an analysis of a numerical pattern is mathematical magic.

Exercise 8.9

1. (a)

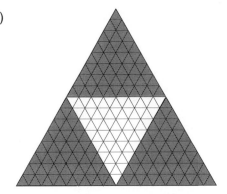

(b)

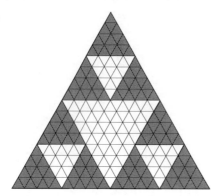 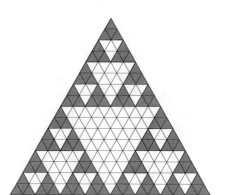

(c)

(d)

Generation number	1	2	3	4	5
No. of triangles (including the unshaded ones)	4	13	40	121	364
Fraction of whole triangle unshaded	$\frac{1}{4}$	$\frac{7}{16}$	$\frac{37}{64}$	$\frac{175}{256}$	$\frac{781}{1024}$

(e) The number of triangles (including the unshaded ones) in the nth generation can be expressed as:

$$\frac{(3^{n+1} - 1)}{2}$$

2. (a)

(b) See diagram above.

(c) The pattern is the same! Amazing isn't it? The explanation could be given as follows, where E is an even number and O is odd:

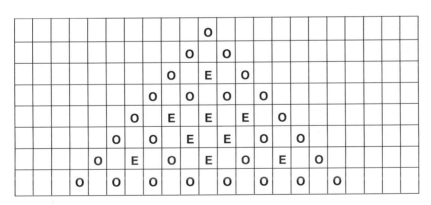

You may also enjoy generating the Sierpinski carpet:

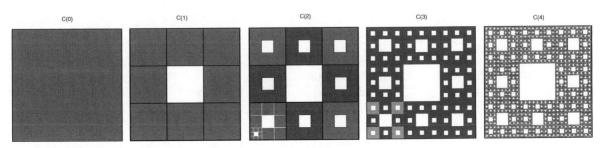

or the Sierpinski pentagon:

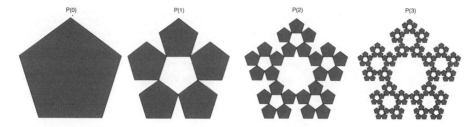

Exercise 8.10: Extension questions

1. Triangle numbers plus 1 $\frac{1}{2}n\,(n+1)+1$

2. 3 × triangle numbers $\frac{3}{2}n\,(n+1)$

3. 2 × odd numbers $2(2n-1)$ or $(4n-2)$

4. 2 × triangle numbers – 1 $(n+1)\,(n+2)-2$ or (n^2+3n)

5. Square numbers – 2 $(n+1)^2-2$

6. 2, 6, 12, 20, 30 $n(n+1)$ or n^2+n

7. 9, 25, 49, 81 $(2n+1)^2$

8. 1, 4, 9, 16 n^2

9. 2, 7, 15, 26, 40 $\frac{1}{2}n(3n+1)$

10. 1, 2, 3, 4, n

Exercise 8.11: Summary exercise

1. (a) 22, 27, 32   (b) $\frac{1}{16}\ \frac{1}{64}\ \frac{1}{256}$ (c) –4, –6, –8

2. (a) 13   (b) 31   (c) $3n+1$

3. (a)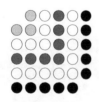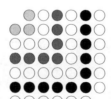

(b)

Pattern no:	Black balls	White balls	Total balls
1	0	2	2
2	4	3	7
3	5	9	14
4	13	10	23
5	14	20	34
6	26	21	47

(c) If n is odd white balls = $\frac{1}{2}n(n + 3) - 1$, blue balls = $\frac{1}{2}n(n + 1)$

If n is even white balls = $\frac{1}{2}(n - 1)(n + 2)$, blue balls $\frac{1}{2} = n(n + 3)$

Total number of balls = $(n + 1)^2 - 2$

4. (a) $S_1 = 17$ (b) $S_4 = 8$ (c) $S_6 = 2$ (d) $S_{10} = -10$

5. (a) 19, 22, 25 $3n+1$
(b) 47, 62, 79 $(n+1)^2 - 2$
(c) −5, −7, −9 $7 - 2n$

6.
```
            1           1
        1 + 1           2
      1 + 2 + 1         4
    1 + 3 + 3 + 1       8
  1 + 4 + 6 + 4 + 1    16
```

(a) 2^{n-1}
(b) 3rd diagonal
(c) 1, 4, 10, 20, 35, they increase in triangle numbers. or are the sum of triangle numbers.
(d) The sum of n triangle numbers

7. (a) (i) 8   (ii) 13   (iii) 21
(b) 144

End of chapter 8 activity: 3D fractals

Practical

Chapter 9: Using formulae

Exercise 9.1

1. $N = x + y$
2. $N = a - b$

3. $A = \dfrac{w + x + y + z}{4}$

4. $P = 14x + 6$
5. $A = 3x\,(4x + 3)$
6. $P = 6x + 2$
7. $A = x(x + 4)$
8. $N = 100(x + y)$

9. $N = \dfrac{x + y}{100}$

10. $N = 10y$
11. $N = ny$

12. $N = \dfrac{nx}{100}$

13. $P = 6a + 6b$
14. $A = 5ab$
15. $P = 10a + 6b$
16. $A = 9ab$
17. $A = x^2 - y^2$
18. $A = xy - (x - 10)(y - 10)$ which simplifies to $A = 10(x + y - 10)$

Exercise 9.2

1. (a) $N = -3$ (c) $N = -1$ (e) $N = 1$
   (b) $N = 2$ (d) $N = -8$ (f) $N = -4$

2. (a) $N = 9$ (c) $N = 13$ (e) $N = -5$
   (b) $N = 2$ (d) $N = -18$ (f) $N = 144$

3. (a) $N = 0.1$ (c) $N = 1.04$ (e) $N = -0.2$
   (b) $N = 0.6$ (d) $N = 0.9$ (f) $N = -7.92$

4. (a) $M = -0.75$ or $-\dfrac{3}{4}$ (c) $M = 12$ (e) $M = 3$

   (b) $M = 0.2$ or $\dfrac{1}{5}$ (d) $M = 8$ (f) $M = -\dfrac{5}{12}$

5. (a) $N = -4$ (c) $N = 4$ (e) $N = 6$
   (b) $N = 8$ (d) $N = -14$ (f) $N = 70$

6. (a) $N = 1.0584$ (c) $N = 0.254016$ (e) $N = 0.1512$
    (b) $N = -0.126$ (d) $N = -1.20204$ (f) $N = 0.9834048$

7. (a) $N = -12$ (c) $N = 36$ (e) $N = 36$
    (b) $N = -4.5$ or $-4\frac{1}{2}$ (d) $N = 3$ (f) $N = -20$

8. (a) $A = 9.6149$ (c) $A = -4.092$ (e) $A = 9.5225$
    (b) $A = -0.444875$ (d) $A = -160$ (f) $A = 0.54$

9. (a) $V = 0.625$ (c) $V = -3.845$ (e) $V = 7.75$
    (b) $V = -1.369$ (d) $V = -8.525$

10. (a) $N = -2.4465$ (c) $N = 1.334025$ (e) $N = 1.9$
    (b) $N = 21.7375$ (d) $N = 0.3625$

Area and volume formulae

This next exercise provides a good opportunity to revise all those formulae that the pupils should know at this stage. Do insist that the pupils set out their answers correctly right from the start.

Exercise 9.3

1. 7.84 cm²
2. 3.7 metres
3. 1.728 m³
4. 0.715 m²
5. 1.053 m³
6. 594 litres
7. 0.63375 m²
8. Area of a kite $= \dfrac{ab}{2}$, area $= 90$ cm²

9. Surface area of a cuboid $= 6x^2$
    Surface area $= 864$ cm²
10. Surface area of a cuboid $= 2wl + 2wh + 2lh = 2(wl + wh + lh)$
    Surface area $= 1376$ cm²

Finding an unknown quantity

If these questions are solved in the way equations are solved they will become simple.

Exercise 9.4

1. 17 cm
2. 19 cm
3. 17 cm
4. 48 cm
5. 7 cm
6. 12 cm
7. 4.57 m
8. 1.6 cm and 3.2 cm
9. 24 cm
10. 3.6 m
11. Base 7.75 cm
12. 12.2 cm
13. 8.66 cm and 11.55 cm
14. 13.4 cm and 22.4 cm
15. 76.4 cm, 107 cm and 122 cm

Polygon formulae

This exercise provides a good opportunity to revise formulae associated with polygons. Make sure that the pupils understand the distinction between regular and irregular polygons.

Exercise 9.5

1. $540°$
2. $1260°$
3. $1080°$
4. $60°$
5. $51.4°$
6. $36°$
7. $108°$
8. $135°$
9. 20
10. 15
11. 12
12. 18

13. (a) $\angle AOB = 72°$
    (b) $\angle OBC = 54°$
    (c) $\angle ABC = 108°$

14. (a) $\angle CDH = 60°$
    (b) $\angle CDE = 120°$
    (c) $\angle DCF = 60°$
    (d) Parallel

15. (a) $\angle EOF = 45°$
(b) $\angle FED = 135°$
(c) $\angle OED = 67.5°$
(d) $\angle BCD = 135°$
(e) $\angle CDB = 22.5°$
(f) $\angle BDE = 112.5°$
(g) Parallel as $BDE + OED = 180°$

16. (a) $\angle CDE = 108°$
(b) $\angle EDF = 120°$
(c) $\angle CED = 36°$
(d) $\angle DEF = 30°$
(e) $\angle CDF = 132°$ or $228°$
(f) $\angle ECF = 60°$

17. 24

Distance, speed and time formulae

Tip: Using the fraction button of the calculator can be helpful in this exercise.

Exercise 9.6

1. 45 miles
2. 1 hour 30 mins
3. 2.25 mph
4. 30 000 mph
5. 2 500 km
6. 40 miles
7. 90 km/h
8. 2 hours 32 minutes
9. 618 mph
10. Average daily distance = 522 km, speed = 21.75 km/h
11. Twice as long
12. 3 times as fast
13. 6 times as fast

Exercise 9.7

1. (a) 41.25 km   (b) 55 km/h

2. (a) $1\frac{5}{6}$ km   (b) 4.4 km/h

3. (a) 220 km   (b) 110 km/h

4. (a) 1250 km   (b) 312.5 km/h

5. 67 mph

6. 90 km/h

7. (a) 110.6 km/h
(b) 3h 37.2 min

Rearranging formulae

This topic goes beyond the Common Entrance syllabus but it still fits into the scheme of work for KS3. It is also a good exercise in pure algebra.

Exercise 9.8

1. $x = y - 3$

2. $x = y + 5$

3. $x = y - 4$

4. $x = 8 - y$

5. $x = y - a$

6. $x = y + b$

7. $x = y - c$

8. $x = d - y$

9. $x = \dfrac{y}{2}$

10. $x = \dfrac{y}{a}$

11. $x = 2y$

12. $x = by$

13. $x = \dfrac{y - 3}{2}$

14. $x = \dfrac{y + 4}{3}$

15. $x = \dfrac{y - 5}{3}$

16. $x = \dfrac{5 - y}{2}$

17. $x = \dfrac{y - a}{3}$

18. $x = \dfrac{y + b}{2}$

19. $x = \dfrac{y - c}{3}$

20. $x = \dfrac{d - y}{3}$

21. $x = \dfrac{y - b}{a}$

22. $x = \dfrac{y + d}{c}$

23. $x = \dfrac{a - y}{b}$

24. $x = \dfrac{y + ab}{a}$ or $\dfrac{y}{a} + b$

25. $x = \dfrac{ay}{3}$

26. $x = \dfrac{by}{a}$

27. $x = \dfrac{2a}{y}$

28. $x = \dfrac{3b}{2y}$

29. $x = \dfrac{ab}{y} + 1$

30. $x = 2y - 2$ or $2(y - 1)$

Units of formulae

This is omitted from the Common Entrance syllabus but, again, is on the KS3 scheme of work. It is a useful exercise to ensure that students do understand how to check their formulae and calculations.

Exercise 9.9

1. (a) $m - d$

    (b) sec $- t$

2. (a) g/cm³ $- D$

    (b) cm³ $- V$

3. (a) Area

    (b) Length

    (c) Length

    (d) Volume

    (e) Length

    (f) Volume

    (g) Area

4. (a) g/m³

    (b) m

    (c) sec

Exercise 9.10: Extension questions – Rearranging formulae with factorising and roots

This exercise should really stretch your scholars. It will also check that they fully understand factorising and the use of squares and square roots.

1. $x = \dfrac{a - yb}{y - 1}$

2. $x = \dfrac{a + yb}{y - 1}$

3. $x = \dfrac{bc - a}{1 + c}$

4. $x = \dfrac{a}{ab + ac - 1}$

5. $x = \dfrac{y - ab + ac}{a + c}$

6. $x = \dfrac{ya - ab}{b + y}$

7. $x = \dfrac{a + by}{b - 1}$

8. $x = \dfrac{cy + ab}{a - c}$

9. $x = \dfrac{a^2 - yb}{y + a}$

10. $x = \dfrac{aby}{a - c + by}$

11. (a) 7   (b) 25   (c) 5

12. (a) 1   (b) 25   (c) 5

13. $x = \sqrt{y^2 + a^2}$ 17. $x = \sqrt{a^2 y^2 - b^2}$

14. $x = \sqrt{a^2 - y^2}$ 18. $x = \dfrac{b}{\sqrt{y^2 - 1}}$

15. $x = \sqrt{\dfrac{y^2 + b^2 a^2}{b}}$ or $\sqrt{\dfrac{y^2}{b} + a^2}$ 19. $x = \sqrt{y^4 - b^2}$

16. $x = \dfrac{ab}{\sqrt{1 - a^2}}$ 20. $x = \sqrt{by^4 + a^2}$

Exercise 9.11: Summary exercise

1. $P = 8a + 12b$

2. $A = 14ab$

3. (a) $N = -3$ (c) $N = 8$ (e) $N = 15$

    (b) $N = -\dfrac{1}{4}$ (d) $N = 1\dfrac{1}{2}$ (f) $N = -12$

4. 32 cm
5. 1.14 cm²
6. 2.67 cm
7. 6.17 cm
8. 12.5 hours

9. (a) $56\dfrac{2}{3}$ km/h   (b) $56\dfrac{2}{3}$ km

10. (a) $x = a - y$ (b) $x = \dfrac{y - c}{a}$ (c) $x = \dfrac{ha - by}{h}$

11. (a) (i) 10 miles   (ii) 1 hour   (iii) 40 mph
    (b) No. He spent 40 min in town and that left him 20 min on the motorway. He must have travelled at 90 mph.

End of chapter 9 activity: Perigal's dissection

Practical
They should all fit together like this:

This is not strictly a 'proof' of Pythagoras' theorem but it will probably convince your class. Unless they can expand brackets they do not have the mathematics to comprehend a formal proof.

If they can expand brackets then the following is probably the simplest (I am indebted to Giles Kirby for this one):

Consider a square of side c (see diagram) inscribed inside a square of side $(a + b)$

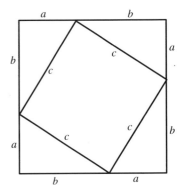

The area of the large square

$$= (a + b)^2$$
$$= a^2 + 2ab + b^2$$

Also the area of the large square

$= $ area of small square $+$ area of 4 triangles

$$= c^2 + 4 \times \frac{1}{2}ab$$

$$= c^2 + 2ab$$

Therefore

$$a^2 + 2ab + b^2 = c^2 + 2ab$$

$$(-2\ ab)$$

$$a^2 + b^2 = c^2$$

Therefore in the right-angled triangle with sides a, b and c the square of the hypotenuse is equal to the sum of the squares of the other two sides!

Chapter 10: Pythagoras' theorem

This introduction to Pythagoras' theorem is also an introduction to the elements of trigonometry. Pupils should be encouraged to get into the habit of making a neat clear sketch, identifying and labelling the hypotenuse before they do anything else.

Exercise 10.1

1.

3.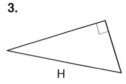

5.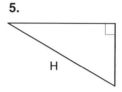

2.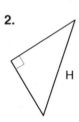

4.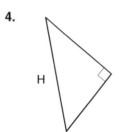

6.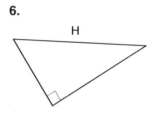

Exercise 10.2

1.   5 cm
2.   7.21 cm
3.   10.8 cm
4.   9.22 m
5.   3 km
6.   2.20 cm
7.   13 cm
8.   2.6 cm
9.   11.3 mm

Exercise 10.3

1.   10 miles
2.   400 km
3.   3.04 km (angle *ABC* is 90º)
4.   John runs 300 m and Janet runs 335 m so Janet runs further.
5.   7.07 cm
6.   No, diagonal is 2.236 m. I must shave 6.4 cm off first.
7.   (a) 5.02 m
         (b) No, the ladder would reach only 39 cm up the wall. The ladder would need to be 5.32 m long.

Exercise 10.4

1. 12 cm
2. 1.59 m
3. 40 m
4. 17.35 m
5. 80 m
6. 1.5 km
7. 11.18 cm
8. 150 m
9. 5.29 m

Exercise 10.5

1. 9.95 cm
2. 25.98 miles
3. 1.87 km
4. 3.87 m
5. 2.24 m
6. 0.97 m
7. 3.54 cm
8. 5.37 cm and 10.73 cm

By now your quicker pupils may want to write out the formula in an abbreviated form. Certainly going straight to the square root can be faster to write down but it can lead to careless mistakes. Potential scholars will benefit from the opportunity to work in roots. For others perhaps the discipline of the stage by stage working is still the safest.

Isosceles triangles

Pupils often make mistakes in this exercise. Commonly they forget to halve the base and forget to subtract the squares.

Exercise 10.6

1. 7.19 cm
2. 5.20 cm
3. 1.32 m
4. 10 cm
5. 9.24 cm

Special triangles

Being able to spot special triangles is essential for those taking scholarship papers. Many papers are non–calculator which can be a bit of a giveaway that a special triangle is being used.

Exercise 10.7

1. 3:4:5 $\Delta \times$ 0.3, $x = 0.9$
2. Not a special triangle, $x = 3.54$
3. 3:4:5 $\Delta \times$ 60, $x = 240$
4. 5:12:13 $\Delta \times$ 5, $x = 65$
5. Not a special triangle, $x = 3.20$
6. 3:4:5 $\Delta \times$ 70, $x = 210$
7. 5:12:13 $\Delta \times$ 15, $x = 195$
8. Not a special triangle, $x = 66.1$

Exercise 10.8

1. 2.5 m
2. 9 m
3. (a) 12 m   (b) 13 m
4. 1300 m
5. 1000 m or 1 km
6. 250 m
7. 12 m

Exercise 10.9

1. $PQ = 5.29$ cm $RS = 4.77$ cm
2. 28.3 cm and 44.7 cm
3. $CD = 7.83$ and $BD = 9.09$ cm
4. (a) No!
   (b) 1.71 cm. Let us hope it is still safe!
5. (a) $CD = 7.07$ cm   (c) $EF = 5$ cm
   (b) $CF = 3.54$ cm   (d) $CG = 2.5$ cm
6. 16.6 cm, but note that there are two different ways of drawing the spider's route on the net.
7. (a) $AB = 3.16$ or $\sqrt{10}$, $AC = 6.08$ or $\sqrt{37}$ and $BC = 5.39$ or $\sqrt{29}$
   (b) No, the square on the longest side is not the sum of the squares on the other two sides.
8. 6.25 km
   Ella worked out that they had turned through a right angle and had walked two sides of a 3 : 4 : 5 triangle (x 1.25)
9. (a) $AC = 17.0$ cm
   (b) $FC = 13.4$ cm
   (c) The areas of triangles: AFB = 36 cm²; BCF = 72 cm²; AFC = 36 cm²
10. Area is 32 cm²

Exercise 10.10: Extension questions – Pythagorean triplets

When looking at these triplets it can be interesting to make up a table to show the last digits of the squares and their sums.

Square numbers only end in the digits: 0, 1, 4, 5, 6, 9, and thus the possible sums are:

	0	1	4	5	6	9
0	0	1	4	5	6	9
1	1	2	5	6	7	0
4	4	5	8	9	3	3
5	5	6	9	0	1	4
6	6	7	0	4	2	5
9	9	0	3	4	5	8

The squares of multiples of 5 end in 0 or 5

If you look at the table, you will see that in one out of three results, of every sum of two squares must be a multiple of 5

That should help the search.

There are of course hundreds of Pythagorean triplets to find and because there is so much information available on the internet this activity should remain in the classroom (preferably one without access to a computer).

A few Pythogrean triplets are:

3 : 4 : 5	8 : 6 : 10	15 : 8 : 17	12 : 16 : 20
5 : 12 : 13	24 : 10 : 26	21 : 20 : 29	16 : 30 : 34
7 : 24 : 25	35 :12 : 37	32 : 24 : 40	27 : 36 : 45
9 : 40 : 41	20 : 48 : 52	48 : 14 : 50	45 : 28 : 53
11 : 60 : 61	40 : 42 : 58	33 : 56 : 65	24 : 70 : 74

Exercise 10.11: Summary exercise

1. For any right–angled triangle the square on the hypotenuse is equal to the sum of the squares on the other two sides.
2. 4.72 km
3. Height = 60.9 cm and area = 975 cm²
4. (a) The length $AD = 6.08$ m
   (b) 7.90 m²
   (c) The length $AE = 2$ m and length $AB = 1.52$ m
   (d) Area $BCFE = 3.95$ m²
5. $BE = 1.86$ m
6. (a) $AD = 5.83$ cm
   (b) Area ABC is 2.7 cm² and area CDE is 1.2 cm²

End of chapter 10 activity: Truthful Twins?

1. (a) Both
   (b) Neither
   (c) Both
   (d) Neither
   (e) Both
   (f) Neither

2. 'If I asked your brother if he always tells the truth what would he say?'
   The truthful twin would say – yes
   The untruthful twin would say – no
   This is the popular mathematical answer but as one of my pupils said, 'you could just ask them what the time is, (as long as you know it) or any other question to which you know the answer.

3. The liar is A.

4. B is the truth teller and A is the liar.

5. At first glance it seems you cannot tell, but then you see B said that A said 'Yes', which is true, so B is the truth teller and A is the liar.

6. A: truthteller
   B: sometimes
   C: liar

7. A: truthteller
   B: liar
   C: sometimes

8. A: sometimes
   B: truthteller
   C: liar

9. A: truthteller
   B: sometimes
   C: liar

10. A: liar
    B: sometimes
    C: truthteller

Chapter 11: Area and volume

Circles

The most common mistakes pupils make is to confuse the formulae for area and volume and to substitute the radius instead of the diameter. It is therefore good discipline to insist that they draw the circle and mark the given length first. They can then do the calculation.

Exercise 11.1

1. (i) The circumference
    (a) 25.1 cm   (d) 28.3 m
    (b) 195 cm   (e) 157 cm
    (c) 3.77 m   (f) 75.4 m
    (ii) The area:
    (a) 50.3 cm²   (d) 63.6 m²
    (b) 3020 cm²   (e) 1960 cm²
    (c) 1.13 m²   (f) 452 m²
2. 2.98 m
3. Area = 154 cm², circumference = 44.0 cm
4. 50.3 cm²
5. 56.5 cm
6. 1.90 m²

Exercise 11.2

1. 231 cm
2. Area = 154 cm² and perimeter = 50.0 cm
3. 1470 cm²
4. (a) 206 m   (b) 2860 m²
5. 283 cm²
6. 193 m²
7. 4.7 m
8. 3770 mm²

Exercise 11.3

1. 4.46 cm
2. 5.64 cm
3. 1.91 m
4. 17.8 cm
5. 113 cm
6. 31.8 cm
7. 1.26 m
8. 7.78 cm

Exercise 11.4

1. (a) 10 cm   (b) 14.1 cm
2. 14.1 cm, 157 cm²
3. 57.1 cm² (Remind the pupils not to work with rounded answers!)
4. (a) 15.6 cm   (b) 69.1 cm²
5. 98 cm²
6. 576 cm²
7. 35.4 cm
8. (a) 9.82 cm²   (b) 1660 cm²   (c) 3.14 cm²
9. (a) $\dfrac{\pi x^2}{2}$ (b) $2x^2$ (c) $2\pi x^2$ (d) $4x^2$

10. (a) 3.46 cm
    (b) 6.93 cm²
    (c) 12.6 cm²
    (d) 2.09 cm²
    (e) 9.31 %
11. (a) 66 cm and 44 cm
    (b) 1.5
    (c) 66
    (d) $73\dfrac{1}{3}$
    (e) 145.2
12. (a) 19.6 cm²
    (b) 7.85 cm
    (c) 1.25 cm
    (d) 4.84 cm
13. 20, 21.5%
14. (a) 110 cm
    (b) 1.10 km
    (c) 909
    (d) 454 (In this question you have to look at whole revolutions, you cannot round up.)
15. (a) 20   (b) 7070 cm   (c) 58.9

Exercise 11.5

1. 33.75 cm³
2. 2.1 m³
3. 1000 cm³
4. Volume = 297 cm³
5. 1.596 m³
6. 6.45 m³
7. (a) The rectangular cross-section
    (b) The triangular section and rectangular section would overflow and the square section would be
        just full.
8. 4320 cm³
9. 8 cm²

10. 20 cm
11. 109 cm³
12. 4.455 m³
13. 1675 cm³

14. 11. 191 cm²

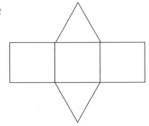

12. 16.5 m²

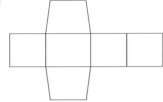

13. 854 cm²

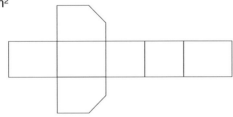

15. (a) 6.28 m²   (b) 314

Exercise 11.6

1. (a) 0.141 litres
(b) 251 000 litres
(c) 141 litres
(d) 5.09 litres
(e) 1.41 litres
(f) 2120 litres
2. 4.83 m³
3. 1140 litres
4. 8
5. 942 cm³

Exercise 11.7

1. 12 cm high and 31.4 cm along, area = 377 cm²
2. (a) 314 cm²   (b) 785 cm³
3. 2750 cm²
4. (a) 150 cm²   (b) strength
5. 683 cm²
6. Cube by 129 cm²
7. The one with radius of 6 cm and a height 5 cm is larger by $30 \times \pi$
8. 22.6 litres
9. 47 bucket loads
10. 15.0 cm

Exercise 11.8

1. (a) 100
   (b) 1 000 000
   (c) 1 000 000
   (d) 0.0001
   (e) 0.000 001
   (f) 0.000 001
2. (a) 1000
   (b) 1 000 000 000
   (c) 1 000 000 000
   (d) 0.000 001
   (e) 0.000 000 001
   (f) 0.000 000 001
3. (a) 1000
   (b) 1 000 000

Exercise 11.9: Extension questions 1

1. 18 cm
2. 1.27 m
3. 9.23 cm
4. 2 cm
5. 19.4 cm
6. 10.6 cm
7. 4 litres
8. 30 (the dimensions of the base are a red herring)

Exercise 11.10: Extension questions 2

1. (a) 5620 cm³
    (b) 3380 cm²

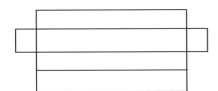

2. 51.7 cm
3. (a) 283 cm³ (b) 2160 cm³ (c) 21.5%
4. (a) 14.2 cm high and radius 6.2 cm; volume = 1710 cm³
    (b) 594 cm³
5. 16.2 cm
6. (a) Height is 15.9 cm and length is 25.1 cm
    (b) 29.7 cm
7. Surface area = 443 cm²; volume = 624 cm³
8. (a) 1 : √3 (b) 8 times
9. (a) 9.27 cm (b) 14.6 cm

10. (a) 4520 cm³
    (b) 25 cm (obviously you add the 0.5 to the top not to the sides).
    (c) 10 cm by 78.5 cm (this assumes you take 25 cm for the diameter – if you take 24 cm it would be too small).
    (d) 630 cm³
    (e) 573 cm³ (you may need to explain how to make icing but if you have got this far a sugary interlude would probably be enjoyed by all)
11. (a) 6.28 m (b) 16 turns (c) 5.03 m³
12. (a) 12 cm by 38.7 cm
    (b) 21 (in these problems about labels you cannot divide the area of the big sheet by the area of the label, you have to see how many labels will go along each side, in this case 7 by 3 is 21 labels).
13. (a) (i) 1 : 1 (ii) The same
    (b) (i) 4 : π (ii) the cylinder by 2.46 cm
14. (a) 123 cm²
    (b) 92.0 cm²
    (c) 401 cm²
    (d) 64.2%
15. (a) 15.72 cm but 15.7 to 3 s.f. (b) 28.5 cm

Exercise 11.11: Summary exercise

1. Area = 1.33 m² ; circumference = 4.08 m
2. Area = 2.05 m² and perimeter = 5.73 m
3. 3.41 times
4. 1800 cm³
5. 4.37 cm
6. (a) 6.17 cm   (b) 9 cm
7. 11.05 cm
8. (a) 3 054 000 litres   (b) 4.14 m   (c) 18.47 m

End of chapter 11 activity: Packaging the litre

Practical

Chapter 12: Simultaneous equations

In this chapter pupils will start to pull together the skills of simplifying, solving and substituting. If you have not revised these techniques first then it would be good to do so. You may also wish to go through scaling up an equation as well as simplifying expressions.

The purely abstract idea of solving the equation by elimination is alien to many pupils of this age, therefore this chapter explores the relationship between equations and graphs first.

Exercise 12.1

1. $x + y = 24$
2. $x - y = 8$
3. $2x + y = 20$
4. $x + y = 15$
5. $25x + 30y = 300$

These last two questions are typical of the types of equation set at this level. Make sure pupils understand that in q.4 you are looking at total number and in q. 5 total price. Pupils will meet more of this in the later exercises.

Exercise 12.2

1. (a)

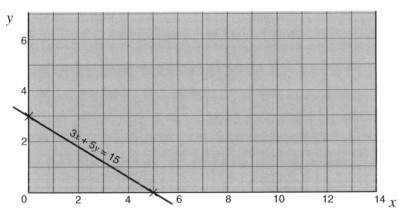

(b)

x	y
0	3
5	0

2. (a)

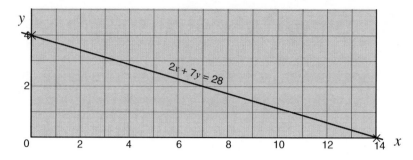

(b)

x	y
0	4
7	2
14	0

3.

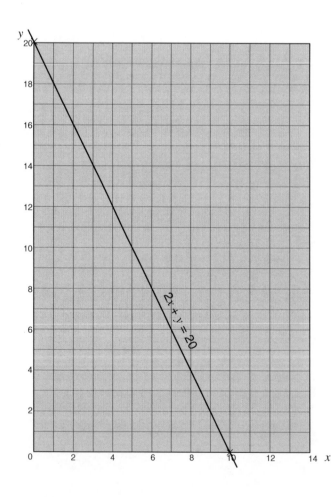

Numbers I could be thinking of:

x	y
0	20
1	18
2	16
3	14
4	12
5	10
6	8
7	6
8	4
9	2
10	0

4.

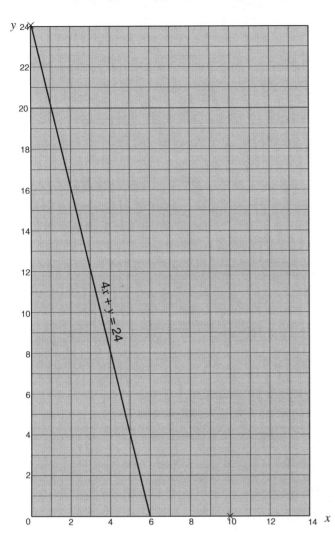

Numbers I could be thinking of:

x	y
0	24
1	20
2	16
3	12
4	8
5	4
6	0

5. (a) $80m + 160j = 800$

$(\div 80)$

$m + 2j = 100$

(b)

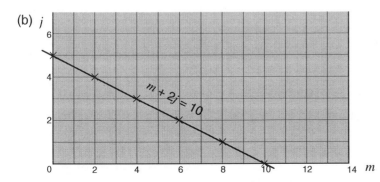

Litres of milk and juice

m	j
0	5
2	4
4	3
6	2
8	1
10	0

(c) 2 litres of milk and 4 litres of juice

6. (a) $450x + 150y = 1350$ ($\div 150$)

     $3x + y = 9$

(b)

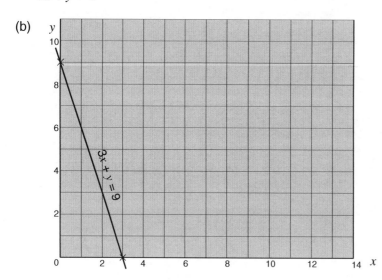

(c)

x	Batteries	y	Batteries
0	0	9	27
1	5	6	18
2	10	3	9
3	15	0	0

(d) 2 packs of long life and 3 packs of normal

7. (a) $15x + 25y = 300$ ($\div 5$)

     $3x + 5y = 60$

(b)

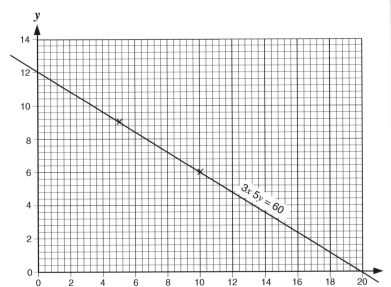

(c)

x	y
0	12
1	11
2	10
3	10
4	9
5	9
6	8
7	7
8	7
9	6
10	6
11	5
12	4
13	4
14	3
15	3
16	2
17	1
18	1
19	0
20	0

(d) I would buy 4 lemons and 8 oranges and would have 40p change.

Exercise 12.3

1. (a) $x = 7, y = 7$ (d) $x = 12, y = 2$ (g) $x = 3, y = 6$

    (b) $x = 14, y = 0$ (e) $x = 0, y = 8$ (h) $x = 5\frac{1}{3}, y = 5\frac{1}{3}$

    (c) $x = 2, y = 2$ (f) $x = 4\frac{1}{2}, y = 9\frac{1}{2}$

2.   (a) $x = 3$, $y = -1$ (c) $x = 6$, $y = 4$
          (b) $x = 8$, $y = 1$ (d) $x = 3$, $y = 6$

3.   (a) $x = -1$, $y = 4$ (c) $x = 2$, $y = 0$
          (b) $x = -3$, $y = 2$ (d) $x = 3$, $y = -1$

4.   (a) $x = 3.2$, $y = 1.4$ (b) $x = 1.4$, $y = -2.4$

5.   (a) $x = -2$, $y = 5$ (b) $x = -1.5$, $y = -3.5$

6.   (a) and (b) The graphs are parallel and so there is no solution.

The elimination method

Make sure that the pupils carefully number each equation. Do make them state (1) + or − (2) on the left. Each solution should end with a 'sub in 1 (or 2)' or a 'check in 2 (or 1)'.

If you start these simple elimination questions insisting on the correct method then the later equations will flow much more easily.

Exercise 12.4

1. $x = 2$, $y = 1$ **4.** $x = 1$, $y = 3$ **7.** $x = 3$, $y = 2$
2. $x = 3$, $y = 4$ **5.** $x = 3$, $y = 3$ **8.** $x = 4$, $y = 3$
3. $x = 5$, $y = 2$ **6.** $x = 3$, $y = 1$ **9.** $x = 1$, $y = 4$

Exercise 12.5

1. $x = 1$, $y = 2$ **4.** $x = 4$, $y = 3$ **7.** $x = 3$, $y = -1$
2. $x = 2$, $y = 1$ **5.** $x = 2$, $y = 5$ **8.** $x = -2$, $y = 5$
3. $x = 3$, $y = 2$ **6.** $x = 4$, $y = 1$ **9.** $x = -1$, $y = -3$

The re-arrangement and substitution methods

There is more than one correct way of solving these problems. The exercise should be accompanied by discussion about which method is the most suitable one to use.

Exercise 12.6

1. $x = 1$, $y = 3$ **5.** $x = 1$, $y = -3$ **9.** $x = -3$, $y = 2\frac{1}{4}$

2. $x = 2$, $y = 7$ **6.** $x = \frac{3}{5}$, $y = -\frac{1}{5}$ **10.** $x = 2\frac{2}{7}$, $y = -1\frac{5}{7}$

3. $x = -2$, $y = 3$ **7.** $x = 1\frac{1}{4}$, $y = 11\frac{1}{2}$ **11.** $x = 3\frac{3}{5}$, $y = 15$

4. $x = -1$, $y = -3$ **8.** $x = 7$, $y = -2\frac{1}{2}$ **12.** $x = 3\frac{1}{2}$, $y = -4$

Exercise 12.7

1. 10 and 15
2. 12 and 16
3. £60, £85
4. $10\frac{1}{2}, 6\frac{1}{2}$

The next few problems are solved by forming one equation for the total number of items and the other for the total price.

5. (a) $c = 6$, $g = 14$
   (b) 6 Coxs and 14 Granny Smiths
6. (a) $p = 14$, $s = 28$
   (b) 98p
7. (a) $c = 35$, $m = 22$
   (b) 57p
8. (a) $x = 12$, $y = 16$
   (b) 192 cm²
9. $t + g = 20$
   $15t + 20g = 365$
   7 Troggles and 13 Gruggles
10. $5m + 9t = 83$
    $2m + 12t = 134$
    Tankies score 12 points, Minkies lose 5 points
    so I score 17 more points for hitting a Tankie than hitting a Minkie
11. $y = 3x - 2$
12. 5 for relations and 10 for friends
13. Half an hour on Lemmings and an hour and a half on Prince of Persia.
14. £3.80
15. 670

Exercise 12.8: Extension questions

1. $x = 5$ $y = -1$ $z = 3$
2. $a = 4$ $b = 2$ $c = \frac{1}{2}$
3. $a = 2$ $b = -3$ $c = 0$
4. 13
5. (a) $3a + 6b + c = 159$
   $a + 7b + 2c = 218$
   $2a + 7b + c = 155$
   $a = 12$ $b = 8$ $c = 75$
   (b) 1 apple, 8 bananas and 1 coconut cost £1.51
6. 7, 7 and 17

7. (a) (i) Two of them combine to make the third
        (ii) No
    (b) (i) Combine two and you get a different value for one unknown
        (ii) No solution

8. $x = 0.585$ to 3 s.f. $y = 1.5$ $z = -0.631$ to 3 s.f.

Exercise 12.9: Summary exercise

1. (a) $x = 0.7$, $y = 5.3$ (b) $x = 8.4$, $y = 9.2$ (c) $x = 6$, $y = 0$
    (d) They are parallel.

2. (a) $x = 3$, $y = 1$ (c) $x = -2$, $y = 3$ (e) $x = 1$, $y = -1$
    (b) $x = 5$, $y = -1$ (d) $x = 2$, $y = -1$ (f) $x = 5$, $y = 1$

3. Clear light bulbs are 50p; pearl light bulbs are 40p.

4. 7 plain sparklers and 3 coloured sparklers

End of chapter 12 activity: A literary genius test

$\frac{1}{2}$ A League, $\frac{1}{2}$ A League, $\frac{1}{2}$ A League, Onwards   (Tennyson, Charge of the Light Brigade)

1 Fish , **2** Fish , Red Fish, Blue Fish   (Dr Seuss)
1 Flew Over The Cuckoo's Nest   (Ken Kesey)
A Tale Of **2** Cities   (Charles Dickens)
3 Sisters   (Anton Checkov)
The **3** Musketeers   (Alexandre Dumas)
4 Quartetes   (T S Elliott)
4.50 From Paddington   (Agatha Christie)
5 Children And It   (E. Nesbit)
Now We Are **6**,   (A A Milne)
The Big **6**   (Arthur Ransome)
Good Old Secret **7**   (Enid Blyton)
I'm Henry The **8**th I Am   (Herman's Hermits)
The **9** Tailors   (Dorothy L Sayers)
12 Dancing Princesses   (The Brothers Grimm)
 Secret Diary Of Adrian Mole Aged **13** And **3** Quarters   (Sue Townsend)
19 Eighty Four   (George Orwell)
20 Thousand Leagues Under The Sea   (Jules Verne)
40 Years On   (Alan Bennet)
101 Dalmations   (Dodie Smith)
1066 And All That   (Sellar and Yeatman)

Chapter 13: Graphs

Exercise 13.1

1.   (a) 50 km/h
    (b) 12.5 km/h

    (c) $8\frac{1}{3}$ km/h

    Rose by car, George by bike and Camilla on foot (for example)

2.   A vehicle travels for 30 minutes at 60 km/h, and then stops for 15 minutes. It then goes for 30 minutes at 80 km/h, and then stops for 45 minutes. The vehicle then returns, travelling for 45 minutes at 40 km/h, stops for 30 minutes then continues for 45 minutes at $53\frac{1}{3}$ km/h.

    The journey takes 4 hours.

3.   (a) One is non stop, one stops several times.
    (b) I hr 18 min
    (c) 50 km
    (d) 70 km/h
    (e) 57 km/h

4.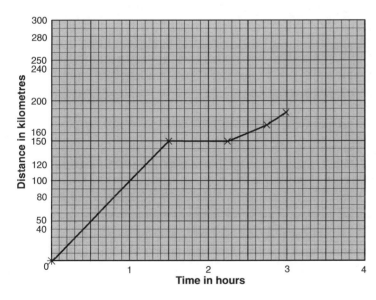

1.   The journey was 185 km.

5.

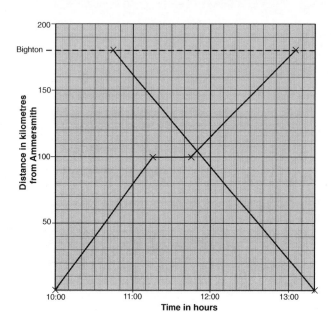

(a) 13:05
(b) She arrived at 13:20, the two cars passed at 11:50

6.

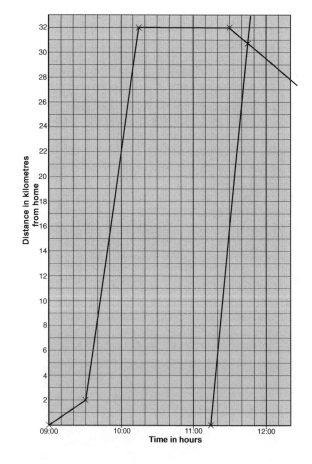

Fred meets his mother at about 11:45

7.

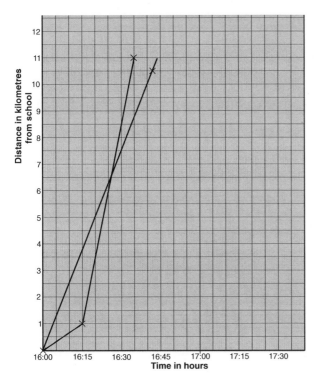

The bus overtakes the bicycle at 16:26

Exercise 13.2

1. (a) Check pupils' answers. Company A should be one whose sales patterns are affected by the summer season and to some degree around Easter. Company B could be one that is experiencing growth overall but experiences minor fluctuations from time to time.
   (b) Answer depends on the pupils' answers to part (a), the influence on April sales is likely to be the effect of Easter occurring around this time.

2. High sales from September, climbing until February, possibly dropping a little. Then climbing again in June July and August as unwary tourists need to buy umbrellas.

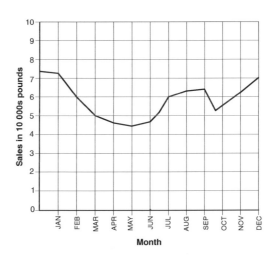

3. Company A – sells computer software. Sales are fairly steady, with a few fluctuations. They rise again after August, as people come back from their holidays and start to pay attention to their IT requirements.

Company B – sells ski clothes. There is very little sales activity over the summer months but as the skiing season approaches sales begin to increase.

Company C – sells bicycles. The sales trend reflects people buying bicycles for the warmer month of the year (spring and summer) and the peak before Christmas could reflect present buying.

Company D – sells swim wear. Sales increase during the summer months and fall away as the colder weather approaches.

4. (a) Starts at 09:00 and ends at 16:00
(b) Some pupils go home for lunch (about 25 of them)
(c) 10%. There is a steady trickle leaving in the morning and afternoon.

5. (a) B (b) D (c) C (d) A

6. (a) C (b) D (c) B (d) A

7. (a) (b) (c) (d)

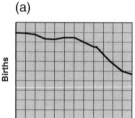 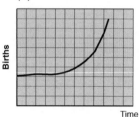 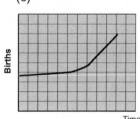 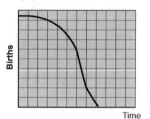

8. Population of Species A steadily grows but then starts to decline rapidly until it is extinct.

Population of Species B steadily grows but at a faster rate than A. It peaks shortly after A has started to decline and declines even faster than A. Soon it is extinct too.

Species B preys on Species A and for a while it seems they live in a balanced community. However it reaches a point where there are so many of Species B that the food supply, Species A, begins to decline and eventually becomes extinct. Species B numbers begin to fall as a result until they too become extinct.

Exercise 13.3

1. (a) (i) $y = 2x$

x	-2	0	5
y	-4	0	10

(iii) $y = \dfrac{x}{2}$

x	-4	0	10
y	-2	0	5

(v) $y = -\dfrac{x}{4}$

x	-4	0	8
y	1	0	-2

(ii) $y = -3x$

x	-3	0	1
y	9	0	-3

(iv) $y = 5x$

x	-1	0	2
y	-5	0	10

(b) – (c)

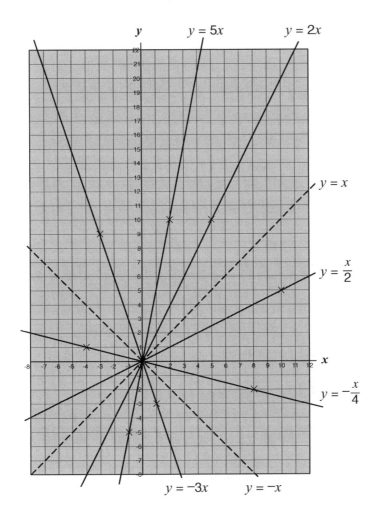

2.   The graphs of $y = x$ and $y = -x$ are at 45° to the axes (they are at 90° to each other). The negative graphs slope downwards and the positive graphs slope upwards to the right. Graphs of fractions of x are less steep. The higher the number before the x, the steeper the graph.

3.

(a) $y = 2x + 4$

x	−4	0	3
y	−4	4	10

(d) $y = 5x + 2$

x	−1	0	1
y	−3	2	7

(b) $y = 3x - 2$

x	−1	0	3
y	−5	−2	7

(e) $y = \dfrac{x}{4} - 3$

x	−4	0	8
y	−4	−3	−1

(c) $y = \dfrac{x}{2} + 3$

x	−4	0	10
y	1	3	8

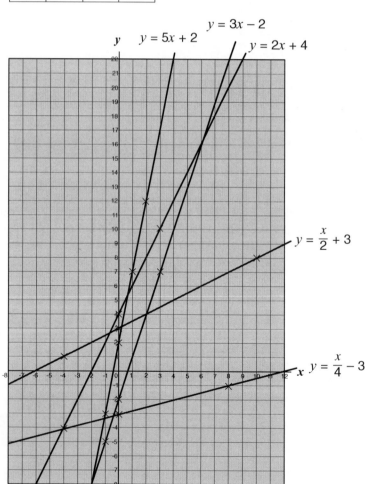

Graphs of curves

It is worth demonstrating graphs of curves using a spreadsheet. By making the increments in x very small, say 0.25, you can really show how the gradient of the curve changes as it crosses the y axis. This does need to be emphasised over and over again, to stop them drawing these with a ruler!

Exercise 13.4

1. $y = x^2 - 1$

x	−3	−2	−1	0	1	2	3
x^2	9	4	1	0	1	4	9
y	8	3	0	−1	0	3	8

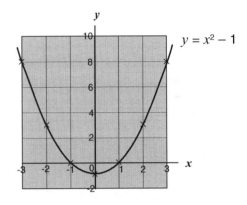

$y = x^2 - 1$

2. $y = x^2 + 2$

x	−3	−2	−1	0	1	2	3
x^2	9	4	1	0	1	4	9
y	11	6	3	2	3	6	11

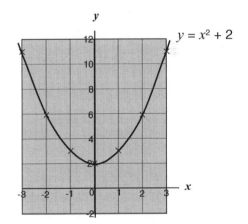

$y = x^2 + 2$

3. $y = 2x^2$

x	−3	−2	−1	0	1	2	3
x^2	9	4	1	0	1	4	9
y	18	8	2	0	2	8	18

$y = x^2 + 2$

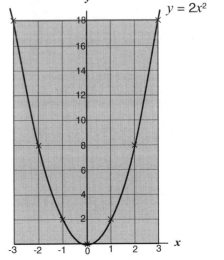

$y = 2x^2$

4. $y = \dfrac{x^2}{2}$

x	−3	−2	−1	0	1	2	3
x^2	9	4	1	0	1	4	9
y	4.5	2	0.5	0	0.5	2	4.5

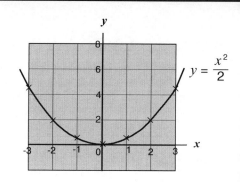

5. $y = 2x^2 - 3$

x	−3	−2	−1	0	1	2	3
x^2	7	4	1	0	1	4	9
y	15	5	−1	−3	−1	5	15

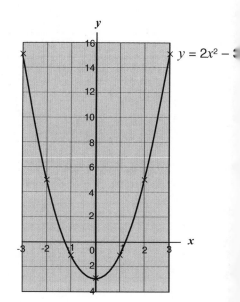

Exercise 13.5

1.

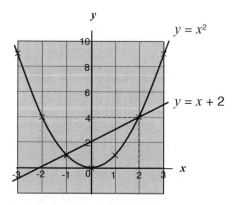

Lines intersect at (2, 4), (−1, 1)

2.

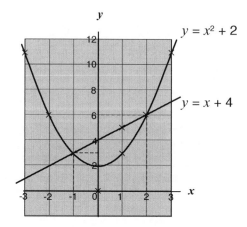

Lines intersect at (2, 6), (−1, 3)

3.

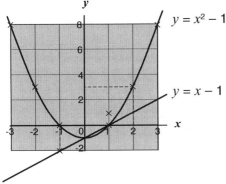

$y = x^2 - 1$

$y = x - 1$

Lines intersect at (0, −1), (1, 0)

5.

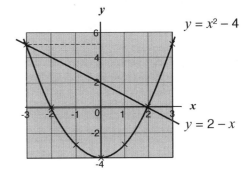

$y = x^2 - 4$

$y = 2 - x$

Lines intersect at (−3, 5), (2, 0)

4.

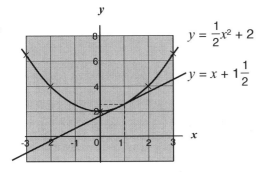

$y = \frac{1}{2}x^2 + 2$

$y = x + 1\frac{1}{2}$

Lines intersect at $(1, 2\frac{1}{2})$, this line just touches the curve so only one result – a tangent!

6.

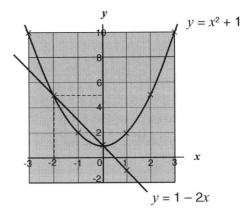

$y = x^2 + 1$

$y = 1 - 2x$

Lines intersect at (0, 1), (−2, 5)

Exercise 13.6: Extension questions 1 – The reciprocal curve

Although this is not on the syllabus, it is an interesting type of graph and one which pupils should be familiar with.

1.

x	−5	−3	−1	−0.5	−0.25	0	0.25	0.5	1	3	5
y	−0.2	−0.33	−1	−2	−4		4	2	1	0.33	0.2

As x gets smaller y becomes bigger.

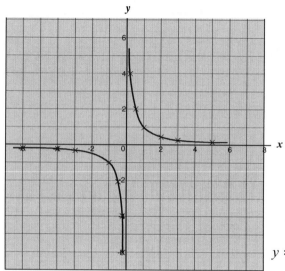

$$y = \frac{1}{x}$$

2. (a)

x	−4	−2	−1	0	1	2	4	6
y	−1	−2	−4		4	2	1	$\frac{2}{3}$

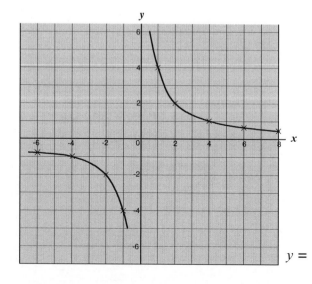

$$y = \frac{4}{x}$$

(b)

x	−6	−4	−2	0	2	4	6	8	10
y	−0.1	−0.125	−1.67	−0.25	−0.5		0.5	0.25	1.67

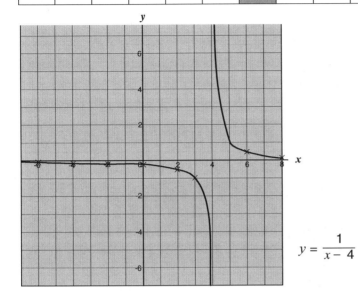

$$y = \frac{1}{x - 4}$$

(c)

x	−3	−2	−1	0	1	2	3	4
y	$\frac{1}{9}$	$\frac{1}{4}$	1		1	$\frac{1}{4}$	$\frac{1}{9}$	$\frac{1}{16}$

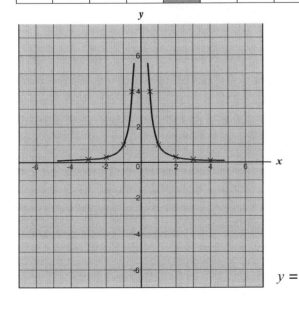

$$y = \frac{1}{x^2}$$

(d)

x	−5	−1	−0.5	−0.25	0	0.25	0.5	1	5
y	−0.1	−0.5	−1	−2		2	1	0.5	0.1

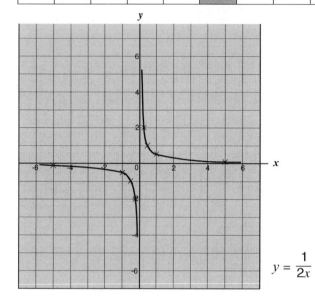

$$y = \frac{1}{2x}$$

(e)

x	−2	−1	$-\frac{1}{2}$	0	$\frac{1}{2}$	1	2	3	4	5
y	$\frac{1}{4}$	$\frac{1}{3}$	0.4	0.5	$0.\dot{6}$	1		−1	$-\frac{1}{2}$	$-\frac{1}{3}$

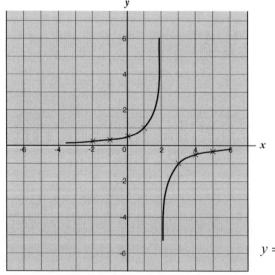

$$y = \frac{1}{2 - x}$$

(f)

x	-3	-2	-1	0	1	2	3	4	$-\dfrac{1}{2}$	$\dfrac{1}{2}$
y	$-\dfrac{1}{9}$	$-\dfrac{1}{4}$	-1		-1	$-\dfrac{1}{4}$	$-\dfrac{1}{9}$	$-\dfrac{1}{16}$	-4	4

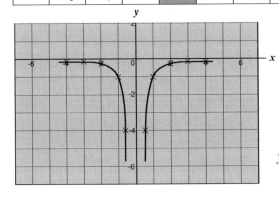

$$y = -\frac{1}{x^2}$$

Exercise 13.7: Extension questions 2 – Other curves

1. $y = x^3$

x	-5	-4	-3	-2	-1	0	1	2	3	4	5
y	-125	-64	-27	-8	-1	0	1	8	27	64	125

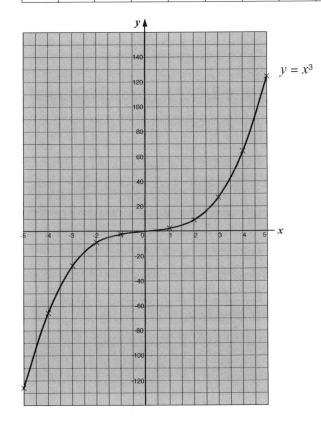

$y = x^3$

2. $y = x^2 - x$

x	−5	−4	−3	−2	−1	0	1	2	3	4	5
x^2	25	16	9	4	1	0	1	4	9	16	25
y	30	20	12	6	2	0	0	2	6	12	20

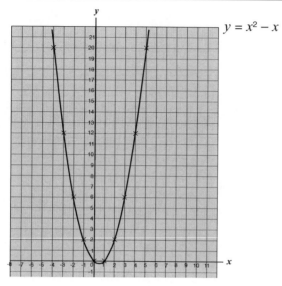

$y = x^2 - x$

3. $y = x^2 + 2x$

x	−5	−4	−3	−2	−1	0	1	2	3	4	5
x^2	25	16	9	4	1	0	1	4	9	16	25
y	15	8	3	0	−1	0	3	8	15	24	35

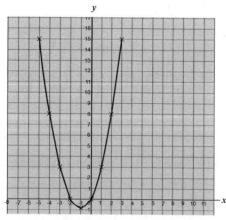

$y = x^2 + 2x$

4. $y = \sqrt{x}$

x	−5	−4	−3	−2	−1	0	1	2	3	4	5
y	*	*	*	*	*	0	1	1.4	1.7	2	2.2

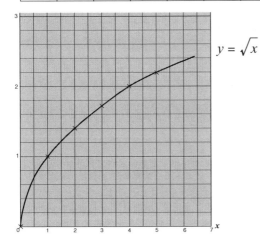

$y = \sqrt{x}$

5. (a) Half the perimeter is 10 and therefore the width must be $10 - x$
$A = x(10 - x) = 10x - x^2$

(b)

x	0	1	2	3	4	5	6	7	8	9	10
x^2	0	1	4	9	16	25	36	49	64	81	10
A	0	9	16	21	24	25	24	21	16	9	0

(c)

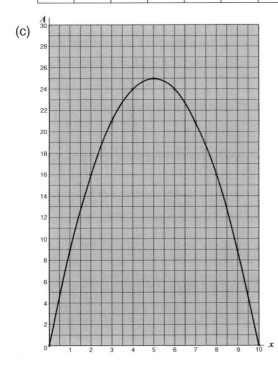

(d) Max area is 25, x is 5 cm and therefore the other side is also 5 cm.

6. (a) The whole surface area is $2x^2 + 4xh = 100$
    This can be rearranged to give h.
(b) Multiply the expression in (a) by x^2
(c) Maximum when V is 68 and $x = 4$

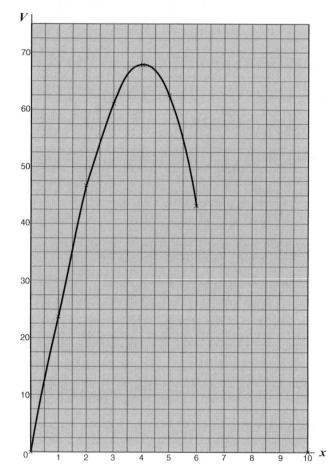

Exercise 13.8: Summary exercise

1. (a) 50 km/h
(b) Stopped for about 1 hour
(c) 50 km/h
(d) 160 km/h
(e) Shopping

2. (a) A   (b) C   (c) D   (d) B

3. $y = 2x - 4$

x	−2	−1	0	1	2
$2x$	−4	−2	0	2	4
y	−8	−6	−4	−2	0

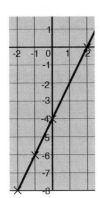

(a) (2, 0)
(b) (0, −4)
(c) (−1, −6)
(d) (−1, −6)

$y = 2x - 4$

4.   (a) $y = x^2 - 1$

x	−3	−2	−1	0	1	2	3
y	8	3	0	−1	0	3	8

$y = x + 1$

x	−2	−1	0	1	2
y	−1	0	1	2	3

(b)–(c)

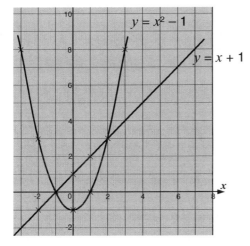

(d) Intersection at (2, 3), (−1, 0)

End of chapter 13 activity: Experiments and graphs

Practical

Chapter 14: Equations and brackets

Most of this chapter deals with multiplying out two brackets. This is on the syllabus for some Scholarship papers but not for ISEB Common Entrance.

Exercise 14.1

1. $9x + 3$
2. $8x - 20$
3. $10 - 6x$
4. $21 + 7x$
5. $12x + 30$

6. $3x^2 + x$
7. $8x^2 - 6x$
8. $5a^2 - 2ab$
9. $5ab + ac$
10. $12x - 9x^2$

Exercise 14.2

1. $3(x + 3)$
2. $4(2x - 3)$
3. $3(5 - x)$
4. $x(7 + x)$
5. $x(x + 2)$

6. $2x(2x + 1)$
7. $2(2x^2 + x + 3)$
8. $3x(2x - 3)$
9. $2(5x^2 - x + 2)$
10. $6(x^2 - 1)$

Exercise 14.3

1. $8x$
2. $10 - x$
3. $16x - 2$
4. $21 - 7x$
5. $15x - 7$

6. $2x^2 + 19x - 3$
7. $4x^2 - x - 15$
8. $35 - 23x - 6x^2$
9. $9 + 5x - 5x^2$
10. $12x - 10x^2 - 15$

11. $3x^2 + 11x + 6$
12. $-15 + 11x - 2x^2$
13. $3a^2 - 3ab + 4a - 4b$

14. $a^2 - b^2$
15. $3 - 3x - 6x^2$
16 $2x^2 - 5xy + 2y^2$

Exercise 14.4

1. $x^2 + 5x + 4$
2. $x^2 + 5x + 6$
3. $x^2 + 10x + 24$
4. $x^2 + 14x + 49$
5. $x^2 + 2x + 1$

6. $x^2 + 7x + 12$
7. $x^2 + 6x + 8$
8. $x^2 + 6x + 9$
9. $x^2 + 11x + 24$
10. $x^2 + 9x + 14$

11. $x^2 - x - 2$
12. $x^2 + x - 6$
13. $x^2 - 4x - 5$
14. $x^2 - 16$
15. $x^2 + 2x - 3$

16. $x^2 + 4x - 12$
17. $x^2 + 2x - 15$
18. $x^2 - 9$
19. $x^2 + x - 20$
20. $x^2 - 1$

21. $x^2 - 3x + 2$
22. $x^2 - 6x + 8$
23. $x^2 - 8x + 15$
24. $x^2 - 8x + 7$
25. $x^2 - 4x + 4$

26. $x^2 - 13x + 40$
27. $x^2 - 8x + 12$
28. $x^2 - 11x + 28$
29. $x^2 - 9x + 20$
30. $x^2 - 2x + 1$

31. $x^2 + 2x - 8$
32. $-x^2 + 5x - 6$
33. $x^2 + 5x + 6$
34. $4 + 4x + x^2$
35. $x^2 - 10x + 9$

35. $x^2 - 25$
37. $6 + x - x^2$
38. $x^2 - 2x - 8$
39. $x^2 - 2x - 15$
40. $9 - 6x + x^2$

Exercise 14.5

1. $x^2 + 4x + 4$
2. $x^2 + 10x + 25$
3. $x^2 - 12x + 36$

4. $9 + 6x + x^2$
5. $16 - 8x + x^2$
6. $1 + 2x + x^2$

7. $x^2 + 8x + 16$
8. $x^2 - 4x + 4$
9. $x^2 + 20x + 100$
10. $x^2 - 16x + 64$

11. $49 - 14x + x^2$
12. $16 + 8x + x^2$
13. $36 - 12x + x^2$
14. $4 + 4x + x^2$

Exercise 14.6

1. $(x - 2)^2$
2. $(x + 3)^2$
3. $(x + 4)^2$
4. $(x - 1)^2$
5. $(x + 7)^2$

6. $(5 - x)^2$
7. $(10 + x)^2$
8. $(b - x)^2$
9. $(b - c)^2$
10. $(x + y)^2$

11. $(2x - 1)^2$
12. $(4x + 1)^2$
13. $(3x + 1)^2$
14. $(2x - 2)^2$
15. $(7x + 7)^2$

16. $(10 - x)^2$
17. $(10 + 2x)^2$
18. $(2b - x)^2$
19. $(3b - c)^2$
20. $(2x + 2y)^2$

Exercise 14.7

1. $x^2 - 9$
2. $x^2 - 16$
3. $x^2 - 1$
4. $x^2 - 25$
5. $x^2 - 49$

6. $4 - x^2$
7. $36 - x^2$
8. $64 - x^2$
9. $a^2 - x^2$
10. $y^2 - x^2$

11. $x^2 - 100$
12. $x^2 - 81$

13. $121 - x^2$
14. $4x^2 - 25$

15. $9x^2 - 9$

16. $4a^2 - x^2$

17. $36 - a^2x^2$

18. $64 - \dfrac{x^2}{4}$

19. $a^2 - \dfrac{x^2}{4}$

20. $y^2 - \dfrac{x^2}{16}$

Exercise 14.8

1. $(x - 3)(x + 3)$
2. $(x - b)(x + b)$
3. $(x - 9)(x + 9)$
4. $(x - 4)(x + 4)$
5. $(x - 10)(x + 10)$

6. $(x - y)(x + y)$
7. $(2x - 1)(2x + 1)$
8. $(3x - 1)(3x + 1)$
9. $(4x - 1)(4x + 1)$
10. $(x - 2a)(x + 2a)$

11. $x^2 + 1$
12. $(2x - b)(2x + b)$

16. $(5x - y)(5x + y)$
17. $(x - 3y)(x + 3y)$

13. $(3x - 5)(3x + 5)$

14. $(12 - x)(12 + x)$

15. $81 + x^2$

18. $(x\sqrt{2} + 3y)(x\sqrt{2} - 3y)$

19. $(x + y\sqrt{6})(x - y\sqrt{6})$

20. $(6x - 11a)(6x + 11a)$

Exercise 14.9

1. $x = 0$ or 4
2. $x = 0$ or 4

3. $x = 0$ or $1\dfrac{1}{4}$

4. $x = -4$ or 4

5. $x = 2$

6. $x = 5$
7. $x = 0$ or 4

8. $x = -5$ or 5

9. $x = 0$ or $1\dfrac{2}{3}$

10. $x = -10$ or 10

11. $x = -4$

12. $x = 0$ or 3

13. $x = 0$ or $-2\dfrac{1}{4}$

14. $x = -6$ or 6

15. $x = 0$ or $\dfrac{3}{5}$

16. $x = -7$

17. $x = 0$ or $\dfrac{5}{8}$

18. $x = -2$ or 2

19. $x = 9$

20. $x = 0$ or $-\dfrac{5}{7}$

21. $x = 4$

22. $x = 0$ or $1\frac{2}{3}$

23. $x = -11$ or 11

24. $x = 3$

25. $x = 0$ or 9

26. $x = -\frac{1}{2}$ or $\frac{1}{2}$

27. $x = -8$

28. $x = 0$ or 15

29. $x = 4$

30. $x = -3$

Exercise 14.10

1. 6 cm, 12 cm
2. 5 cm, 20 cm
3. 7, 13
5. 9, 11
6. 5 cm, 5 cm
7. 3 cm, 6 cm
8. $x = 4$
9. 4, 9
10. 8 cm, 11 cm

Exercise 14.11: Extension questions

1. (a) (i) $2n + 1$ (ii) always odd
(b) (i) 1   (ii) always 1 i.e. odd
(c) (i) $n^2 + n$ (ii) always even

2. (a) (i) $3n$ (ii) 3, 1 and n
(b) (i) $n^3 - n$ (ii) always even

3. (a) $p^2 - q^2$
(b) $p = 5$, $q = 4$
(c) (i) $p = 5$, $q = 3$ (ii) $p = 13$, $q = 12$
(d) (i) $3^2 + 4^2 = 5^2$ (i) $5^2 + 12^2 = 13^2$
     when $(p + q)(p - q) = 144$, $p = 13$, $q = 5$

4. (a) Check pupil's sketch (b) $625 - 50x + x^2$
(c) 8 cm, 15 cm, 17 cm

5. (a) Even number $= 2x$ then $+1$
(b) $4x^2 + 4x + 1$
(c) $4(x^2 + x) + 1$
(d) 0
(e) (iii) 523 and (v) 1067 have remainder 3 when divided by 4
(Note 517 has remainder 1 when dividing by 4 but is NOT a perfect square.)

6. (a) $(a - b)^2 = a^2 - 2ab + b^2$

(b) (i) $23\dfrac{1}{25}$

(ii) $x^2 - \dfrac{2}{5}x + \dfrac{1}{25}$

(iii) $x^2 - 2 + \dfrac{1}{x^2}$

(c) If $x = 1$, $(x - \dfrac{1}{x})^2 = 0$, If $x > 1$ or $x < 1$ then $x^2 > 2 - \dfrac{1}{x^2}$

(d) 2

(e) 1

7. (a) $4ab$
    (b) $(a + b) = 5$ $(a - b) = 3$; $(a + b) = -5$ $(a - b) = -3$; $(a + b) = 4$ $(a - b) = 0$
    (c) $a = 4$ $b = 1$, $a = 1$ $b = 4$, $a = 2$ $b = 2$

8. (a) $4xy$
    (b) $xy = 30$ so if $x = 30$ $y = 1$ $m = 31$ $n = 29$

    (c) if $x = 15$ $y = 2$, $m = 17$ $n = 13$
    if $x = 6$ $y = 5$, $m = 11$ $n = 1$

9. (a) $p^2 - q^2$
    (b) (i) $11 = 6^2 - 5^2$ (ii) $19 = 10^2 - 9^2$
    (c) 15 and 16

    (d) $18\dfrac{1}{2}$, $17\dfrac{1}{2}$; 10, 8; $7\dfrac{1}{2}$, $4\dfrac{1}{2}$; $6\dfrac{1}{2}$, $2\dfrac{1}{2}$; 6, 0

10. (a) (i) $(6 + 4\sqrt{2})$ (ii) $(6 - 4\sqrt{2})$

    (b) (i) $(m^2 + m + 2m\sqrt{m})$ and (ii) $(m^2 + m - 2m\sqrt{m})$

Exercise 14.12: Summary exercise

1. (a) $6 - 6x^2$
    (b) $7b + 4$
    (c) $-a - 4$
    (d) $2x^2 + 9$

2. (a) $x(9 + x)$
    (b) $3a(4 + a)$
    (c) $5(2x^2 - x + 3)$
    (d) $6(6x^2 - 1)$

3. (a) $x^2 + 4x + 3$
    (b) $x^2 + 3x - 28$
    (c) $10 + 3b - b^2$
    (d) $5a - 5b + ab - a^2$

4. (a) $x^2 + 10x + 25$
    (b) $x^2 - 12x + 36$
    (c) $25 - 10a + a^2$
    (d) $4a^2 - 4ab + b^2$

5. (a) $(x - 3)^2$
    (b) $(a + 5)^2$

6. (a) $x^2 - 25$
    (b) $x^2 - 49$
    (c) $36 - a^2$
    (d) $4a^2 - b^2$

7. (a) $(x - 6)(x + 6)$
    (b) $(a - 12)(a + 12)$

8. 35

End of chapter 14 activity: The dragon curve or Jurassic Park fractal

The joy of this fractal for the prep school child is fairly obvious. It is very simple to generate but not quite as simple as it looks, because it matters how you fold the paper.
It can be quite hard when working in pairs to see exactly how to put the fractal together. It can generate a lot of discussion on clockwise, anticlockwise, rotation and reflection. When it becomes impossible to do mechanically one has to revert to the theory.

The basic table generates a sequence that leads to an unusual formula.

Large fractals can make a great classroom display!

Iteration	Number of Lines	Number of Points
0	1	2
1	2	3
2	4	5
3	8	9
4	16	17
5	32	33
6	64	65

Practical materials:

This exercise can be done with folded paper but it is difficult to stick down. It could be done simply by copying the fold onto centimetre squared paper and using a different colour for each iteration. For an eye catching display, you can use pipe cleaners!

Chapter 15: Probability

Exercise 15.1

1. (a) $\frac{1}{2}$ (d) $\frac{1}{13}$

    (b) $\frac{1}{4}$ (e) $\frac{3}{4}$

    (c) $\frac{10}{13}$ (f) $\frac{1}{52}$

2. (a) $\frac{1}{6}$ (c) $\frac{1}{2}$

    (b) $\frac{1}{3}$ (d) $\frac{5}{6}$

3. (a) $\frac{5}{26}$ (b) $\frac{21}{26}$ (c) $\frac{4}{13}$

4. (a) $\frac{4}{11}$ (c) $\frac{1}{11}$

    (b) $\frac{2}{11}$ (d) 0

5. (a) $\frac{11}{18}$ (b) $\frac{11}{18}$

6. (a) $\frac{3}{7}$ (b) 9

7. (a) $\frac{5}{12}$ (b) $\frac{5}{12}$

8. (a) $\frac{2}{5}$ (b) $\frac{1}{5}$ (c) $\frac{1}{5}$ (d) 0

    (e) $\frac{11}{20}$ (f) $\frac{7}{10}$

Exercise 15.2

1. 36
2. 48
3. 13 or 14
4. 6
5. (a) 10
   (b) probably not, hairbrushes usually land bristles up
6. (a) 10   (b) 30   (c) 20

7. (a) $\frac{1}{50}$ (b) 50   (c) 981

8. $\frac{3}{25}$ No

There is a good opportunity to play some games of chance here.

Exercise 15.3

1. (a) $\dfrac{2}{13}$ (b) $\dfrac{7}{13}$ (c) $\dfrac{2}{13}$ (d) $\dfrac{7}{26}$ (e) $\dfrac{1}{13}$ (f) $\dfrac{8}{13}$

2. (a) $\dfrac{1}{30}$ (b) $\dfrac{1}{5}$ (c) $\dfrac{1}{3}$ (d) $\dfrac{1}{2}$ (e) $\dfrac{8}{15}$

3. (a) (i) $\dfrac{5}{17}$ (ii) $\dfrac{4}{17}$

   (b) (i) $\dfrac{7}{17}$ (ii) $\dfrac{4}{17}$

   (c) (i) $\dfrac{3}{17}$ (ii) $\dfrac{6}{17}$

4. (a) $\dfrac{5}{12}$ (b) $\dfrac{5}{11}$ (c) $\dfrac{1}{2}$ (d) 5

5. (a) $\dfrac{7}{47}$ (b) $\dfrac{40}{47}$

6. (a) $\dfrac{10}{47}$ (b) $\dfrac{13}{47}$

7. (a) $\dfrac{2}{9}$ (b) $\dfrac{11}{26}$ (c) $\dfrac{12}{23}$

8. (a) $\dfrac{1}{4}$ (b) $\dfrac{59}{239}$ (c) (i) $\dfrac{1}{8}$ (ii) $\dfrac{30}{239}$

9. (a) $\dfrac{15}{32}$ (b) $\dfrac{5}{31}$ (c) $\dfrac{11}{31}$

10. (a) $\dfrac{10}{37}$ (b) $\dfrac{1}{4}$

   (c) Genie took diamonds. You cannot tell what Aladdin took, except it was not diamonds.
   (d) They both took emeralds.

Exercise 15.4

1.

		First die					
		1	2	3	4	5	6
Second die	1	(1,1)	(2,1)	(3,1)	(4,1)	(5,1)	(6,1)
	2	(1,2)	(2,2)	(3,2)	(4,2)	(5,2)	(6,2)
	3	(1,3)	(2,3)	(3,3)	(4,3)	(5,3)	(6,3)
	4	(1,4)	(2,4)	(3,4)	(4,4)	(5,4)	(6,4)
	5	(1,5)	(2,5)	(3,5)	(4,5)	(4,5)	(6,5)
	6	(1,6)	(2,6)	(3,6)	(4,6)	(5,6)	(6,6)

(a) $\frac{1}{12}$ (b) $\frac{7}{12}$ (c) $\frac{1}{6}$ (d) $\frac{1}{2}$

2.   (a) $\frac{5}{12}$ (b) $\frac{3}{4}$

3.

	First die					
	1	2	3	4	5	6
1	(1,1)	(2,1)	(3,1)	(4,1)	(5,1)	(6,1)
1	(1,1)	(2,1)	(3,1)	(4,1)	(5,1)	(6,1)
1	(1,1)	(2,1)	(3,1)	(4,1)	(5,1)	(6,1)
2	(1,2)	(2,2)	(3,2)	(4,2)	(5,2)	(6,2)
2	(1,2)	(2,2)	(3,2)	(4,2)	(5,2)	(6,2)
3	(1,3)	(2,3)	(3,3)	(4,3)	(5,3)	(6,3)

(Second die)

(a) $\frac{1}{12}$ (b) $\frac{11}{18}$ (c) $\frac{1}{6}$ (d) $\frac{1}{18}$ (e) $\frac{5}{9}$ (f) $\frac{4}{9}$

4.

	First die					
	1	2	3	4	5	6
1	(1,1)	(2,1)	(3,1)	(4,1)	(5,1)	(6,1)
2	(1,2)	(2,2)	(3,2)	(4,2)	(5,2)	(6,2)
3	(1,3)	(2,3)	(3,3)	(4,3)	(5,3)	(6,3)
4	(1,4)	(2,4)	(3,4)	(4,4)	(5,4)	(6,4)
5	(1,5)	(2,5)	(3,5)	(4,5)	(5,5)	(6,5)
6	(1,6)	(2,6)	(3,6)	(4,6)	(5,6)	(6,6)
7	(1,7)	(2,7)	(3,7)	(4,7)	(5,7)	(6,7)
8	(1,8)	(2,8)	(3,8)	(4,8)	(5,8)	(6,8)

(Second die)

(a) $\frac{1}{16}$ (b) $\frac{1}{16}$ (c) $\frac{1}{8}$ (d) $\frac{1}{4}$ (e) $\frac{19}{48}$

(f) 7, 8 and 9 are equally likely, each has a probability of $\frac{1}{8}$

5.

	First spinner			
	1	2	3	4
1	(1,1)	(2,1)	(3,1)	(4,1)
2	(1,2)	(2,2)	(3,2)	(4,2)
2	(1,2)	(2,2)	(3,2)	(4,2)
3	(1,3)	(2,3)	(3,3)	(4,3)
4	(1,4)	(2,4)	(3,4)	(4,4)
4	(1,4)	(2,4)	(3,4)	(4,4)

Second spinner

(b) (i) 8 and 2   (ii) 5   (iii) $\frac{1}{2}$ (iv) $\frac{1}{2}$ (v) $\frac{1}{6}$ (vi) $\frac{5}{24}$

6. (a)

	First pile			
	A♠	A♥	A♦	A♣
K♠	A♠K♠	A♥K♠	A♦K♠	A♣K♠
K♥	A♠K♥	A♥K♥	A♦K♥	A♣K♥
K♦	A♠K♦	A♥K♦	A♦K♦	A♣K♦
K♣	A♠K♣	A♥K♣	A♦K♣	A♣K♣

Second pile

(a) $\frac{1}{4}$ (b) $\frac{1}{2}$ (c) $\frac{1}{4}$ (d) 0

Exercise 15.5: Extension questions – Drawing diagrams to help solve problems

1.

	Girls	Boys	Total
Pets	7	9	16
No Pets	5	1	6
Total	12	10	22

(a) $\frac{6}{11}$ (b) $\frac{8}{11}$ (c) $\frac{9}{22}$

2. (a)

	Girls	Boys	Total
Board	60	70	130
Day	90	20	110
Total	150	90	240

(b) $\frac{1}{12}$ (c) $\frac{9}{11}$

3.

	Coq	Omelette	Total
Caramel	35	14	49
Glace	8	29	37
Total	43	43	86

(a) 35   (b) $\dfrac{29}{86}$

4.

	Girls	Boys	Total
Trousers	16.5	27	43.5
Skirts	38.5	0	38.5
Shorts	0	18	18
Total	55	45	100

(a) $\dfrac{7}{10}$ (b) $\dfrac{2}{5}$ (c) $\dfrac{87}{200}$ or 43.5%

5. (a)

	1 person	2 people	More than 2	Total
Child	0	15	80	95
No child	4	1	0	5
Total	4	16	80	100

(b) 15%   (c) 0   (d) 1%

6.

	Girls	Boys	Total
Walk			$\dfrac{1}{3}$
Car			$\dfrac{1}{4}$
Public trans			$\dfrac{5}{12}$
Total	$\dfrac{1}{2}$	$\dfrac{1}{2}$	1

$\dfrac{5}{24}$ if you assume that the boys and girls are exactly half in each category. If not you need more information.

Exercise 15.6: Summary exercise

1. (a) $\frac{1}{13}$ (b) $\frac{1}{4}$ (c) $\frac{1}{52}$ (d) $\frac{2}{13}$ (e) $\frac{4}{13}$

2. (a) $\frac{3}{8}$ (b) $\frac{1}{2}$ (c) $\frac{3}{4}$

3. (a)

	First die					
	1	2	3	4	5	6
1	(1,1)	(2,1)	(3,1)	(4,1)	(5,1)	(6,1)
2	(1,2)	(2,2)	(3,2)	(4,2)	(5,2)	(6,2)
3	(1,3)	(2,3)	(3,3)	(4,3)	(5,3)	(6,3)
3	(1,3)	(2,3)	(3,3)	(4,3)	(5,3)	(6,3)
5	(1,5)	(2,5)	(3,5)	(4,5)	(5,5)	(6,5)
6	(1,6)	(2,6)	(3,6)	(4,6)	(5,6)	(6,6)

(Second die — row labels at left)

(b) (i) $\frac{1}{6}$ (ii) $\frac{5}{18}$ (iii) $\frac{25}{36}$ (iv) $\frac{1}{12}$ (c) 5

4. (a) $\frac{3}{10}$ (b) $\frac{2}{9}$ (c) $\frac{1}{3}$ (d) 8

5. 9

6. (a)

	Prep set	No prep	Total
Hand in	56	14	70
No hand in	24	6	30
Total	80	20	100

(i) 6%   (ii) 24%   (iii) 14%

(b) 22.4%   (c) 4 or more likely 5

End of chapter 15 activity: Probability experiments

Practical

Chapter 16: Transformations

This chapter takes a more formal approach to transformations, including the construction of reflections and rotations. The aim is to get students to see beyond the obvious.

Exercise 16.1

1. (a)

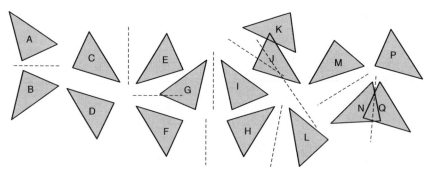

(b) A and B   C and E   E and F   G and I   I and K
     M and N   H and M   N and Q   F and H   H and L

2. (a)

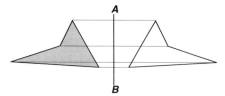

(b)

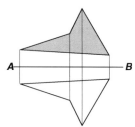

(c)

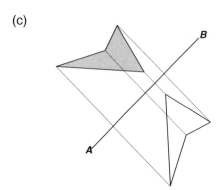

3. Check pupils' own drawings.

4.

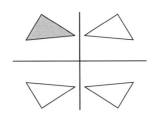 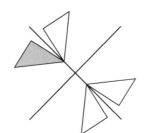

5.

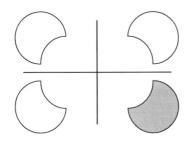 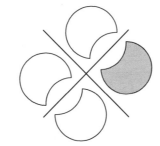

6.

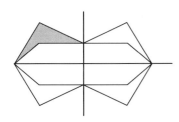 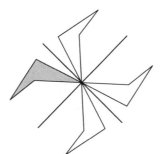

7.

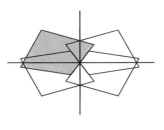 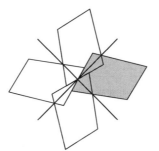

8. Check pupils' own designs.

Exercise 16.2

1.

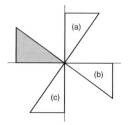

2.

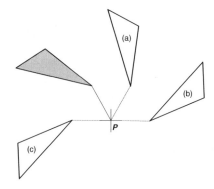

3.

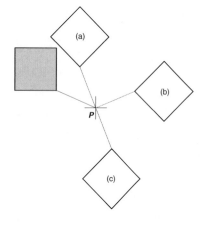

4. Check pupils' own drawings.

Exercise 16.3

1. Order of rotational symmetry and lines of symmetry:

 (a) 2   2
 (b) 2   2
 (c) 4   4
 (d) none   1
 (e) none   1

2. Order of rotational symmetry and lines of symmetry:

 (a) none   1
 (b) 2   2
 (c) 6   0
 (d) 2   2
 (e) 3   3

3. Order of rotational symmetry and lines of symmetry:

(a) 2   0

(b) 2   2

(c) 4   0

(d) none   0

(e) 3   0

4. In questions 4-6 the answers given are examples – they are not the only possible answers.

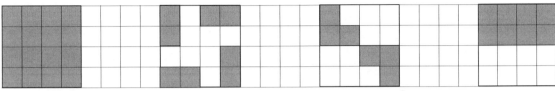

| 4 lines of symmetry, rotational symmetry of order 4 | 0 lines of symmetry, rotational symmetry of order 4 | 0 lines of symmetry, rotational symmetry of order 2 | 1 lines of symmetry and no rotational symmetry |

5.

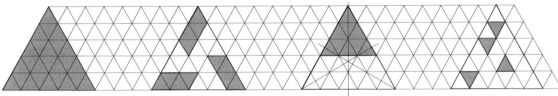

| 3 lines of symmetry, rotational symmetry of order 3 | 0 lines of symmetry, rotational symmetry of order 3 | 1 line of symmetry and no rotational symmetry | No lines of symmetry and no rotational symmetry |

6.

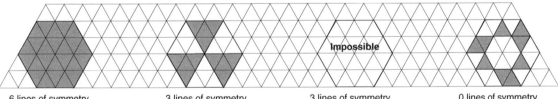

| 6 lines of symmetry, rotational symmetry of order 6 | 3 lines of symmetry, rotational symmetry of order 3 | 3 lines of symmetry and no rotational symmetry | 0 lines of symmetry, rotational symmetry of order 3 |

Impossible

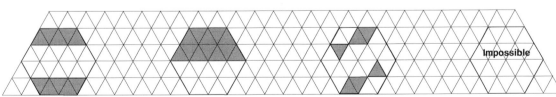

| 2 lines of symmetry, rotational symmetry of order 2 | 1 line of symmetry and no rotational symmetry | No lines of symmetry, rotational symmetry of order 2 | 2 lines of symmetry and no rotational symmetry |

Impossible

Exercise 16.4

1. $A = \begin{pmatrix} 3 \\ -3 \end{pmatrix}$ $E = \begin{pmatrix} 3 \\ 2 \end{pmatrix}$ $I = \begin{pmatrix} 2 \\ 0 \end{pmatrix}$ $M = \begin{pmatrix} 2 \\ -1 \end{pmatrix}$

   $B = \begin{pmatrix} -3 \\ 3 \end{pmatrix}$ $F = \begin{pmatrix} -3 \\ -2 \end{pmatrix}$ $J = \begin{pmatrix} -4 \\ 0 \end{pmatrix}$

   $C = \begin{pmatrix} 0 \\ 2 \end{pmatrix}$ $G = \begin{pmatrix} 2 \\ -3 \end{pmatrix}$ $K = \begin{pmatrix} -3 \\ -3 \end{pmatrix}$

   $D = \begin{pmatrix} 0 \\ -3 \end{pmatrix}$ $H = \begin{pmatrix} -4 \\ 3 \end{pmatrix}$ $L = \begin{pmatrix} 1 \\ -3 \end{pmatrix}$

2.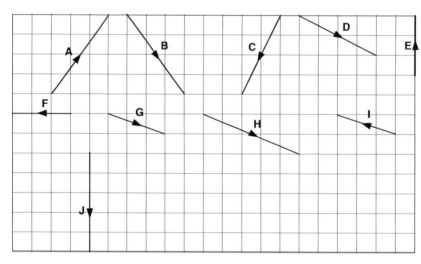

3.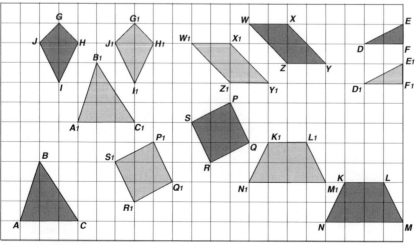

4. (a)

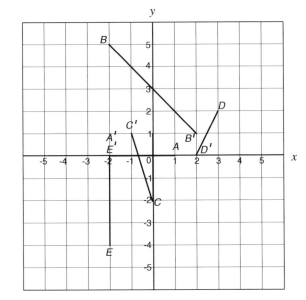

(b) $A'(-2, 0)$
 $B'(2, 1)$
 $C'(-1, 1)$
 $D'(2, 0)$
 $E'(-2, 0)$

5. (a) $A'(1, 6)$
 (b) $B'(-2, 1)$
 (c) $C'(-1, -1)$
 (d) $D'(-3, 3)$
 (e) $E'(2, -5)$

6.

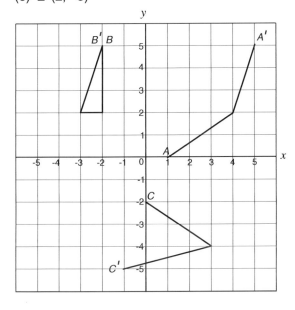

(a) $A'(5, 5)$
(b) $B'(-2, 5)$
(c) $C'(-1, -5)$

Exercise 16.5

1.

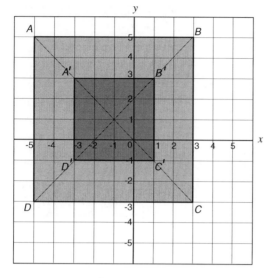

Scale factor $\times \dfrac{1}{2}$

Centre of enlargement (−1, 1)

2.

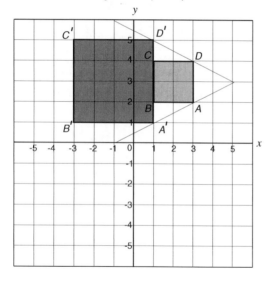

Scale factor ×2
Centre of enlargement (5, 3)

3.

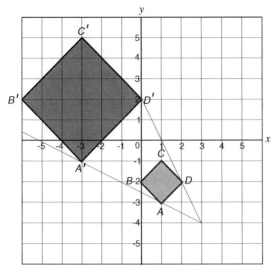

Scale factor ×3
Centre of enlargement (3, −4)

4.

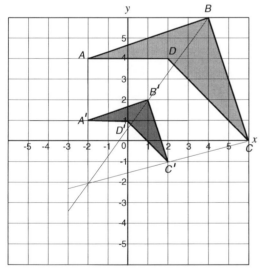

Scale factor $\times \dfrac{1}{2}$
Centre of enlargement (−2, −2)

5.

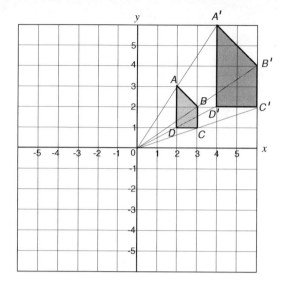

Scale factor ×2
Centre of enlargement (0, 0)

6.

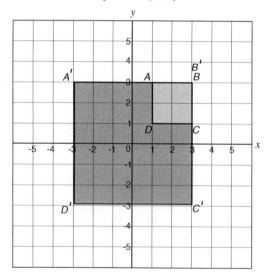

Scale factor ×3
Centre of enlargement (3, 3)

7.

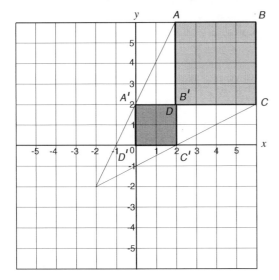

Scale factor $\times \dfrac{1}{2}$

Centre of enlargement (−2, −2)

8.

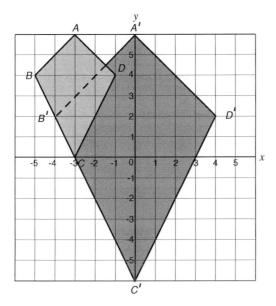

Scale factor ×2

Centre of enlargement (−6, 6)

Exercise 16.6

1. (a) a reflection in the line $y = 1.5$
   (b) a rotation of 180° about the point (−1, −2)

   or

   a rotation of 90° clockwise about the point (−1, −6)

   or

   a rotation of 90° anticlockwise about the point (−1, 2)

   (c) a translation by the vector $\begin{pmatrix} 8 \\ -3 \end{pmatrix}$

   (d) an enlargement of scale factor 2 and centre (0, 1)

   (e) an enlargement of scale factor $\frac{1}{2}$ and centre (0, 1)

2. (a) a reflection in the line $y = 2$

   (b) a translation by the vector $\begin{pmatrix} -6 \\ 2 \end{pmatrix}$

   (c) a rotation of 90° clockwise about the point (−4, −2)

   or

   a reflection in $y = x + 2$
   (d) an enlargement of scale factor 2 and centre (−5, −2)
   (e) a rotation of 90° clockwise about the point (2, −2)

   or

   a reflection in the line $y = -x$

3. (a) a translation by the vector $\begin{pmatrix} -6 \\ -2 \end{pmatrix}$

   (b) a rotation of 180° about the point (−3.5, 2)
   (c) an enlargement of scale factor 2 and centre (−5, 3)

   (d) an enlargement of scale factor $\frac{1}{2}$ and centre (−5, 3)

   (e) a reflection in the line $y = x$
   (f) a rotation of 90° anticlockwise about the point (−1, 1)

4. (a) a reflection in the line $x = 1$
   (b) a rotation of 90° anticlockwise about the point (1, −1)

   (c) an enlargement of scale factor $\frac{1}{2}$ and centre (1, 1)

   (d) a translation by the vector $\begin{pmatrix} -1 \\ -6 \end{pmatrix}$

   (e) a reflection in the line $y = -x$

5.   (a) (b) (c)

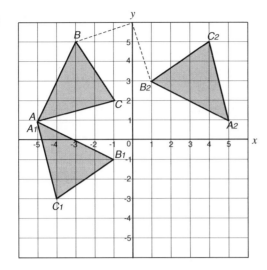

(d) a rotation of 90° anticlockwise about (0, 6)

6.   (a) (b) (c)

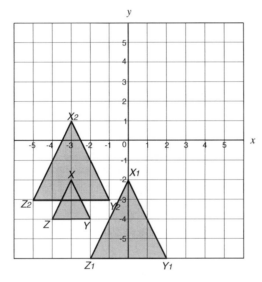

(d) a translation by the vector $\begin{pmatrix} -3 \\ 4 \end{pmatrix}$

7. (a) (b) (c)

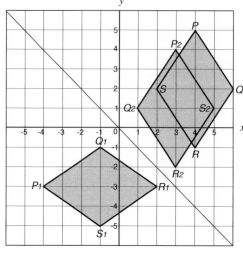

(d) a translation by the vector $\begin{pmatrix} -1 \\ -1 \end{pmatrix}$

8. (a) (b) (c)

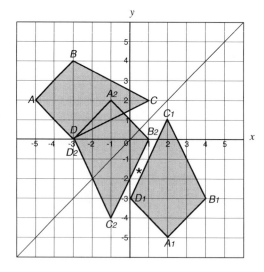

(d) a rotation of 180° about $(\frac{1}{2}, -1\frac{1}{2})$

9. (a) (b) (c)

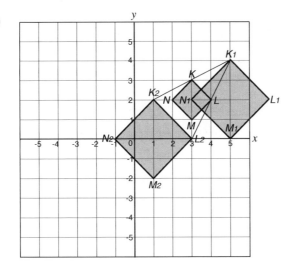

(d) an enlargement by scale factor $\frac{1}{2}$ and centre (5, 4)

10. (a) (b) (c)

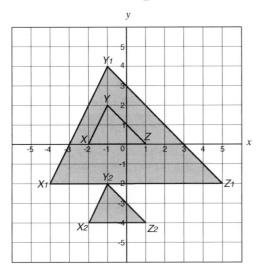

(d) an enlargement by scale factor 3 and centre (−1, −5)

Exercise 16.7: Extension questions

1. A reflection in the x axis.

A	A_1	B	B_1
(4, 5)	(4, −5)	(−5, 4)	(−5, −4)
(5, 1)	(5, −1)	(−5, 1)	(−5, −1)
(1, 2)	(1, −2)	(−2, 2)	(−2, 2)
(a, b)	$(a, -b)$	(a, b)	$(a, -b)$

2. A reflection in the y axis.

A	A_2	B	B_2
(4, 5)	(−4, 5)	(−5, 4)	(5, 4)
(5, 1)	(−5, 1)	(−5, 1)	(5, 1)
(1, 2)	(−1, 2)	(−2, 2)	(2, 2)
(a, b)	$(-a, b)$	(a, b)	$(-a, b)$

3. A reflection in the line $y = x$

A	A_3	B	B_3
(4, 5)	(5, 4)	(−5, 4)	(4, −5)
(5, 1)	(1, 5)	(−5, 1)	(1, −5)
(1, 2)	(2, 1)	(−2, 2)	(2, −2)
(a, b)	(b, a)	(a, b)	(b, a)

4. A reflection in the line $y = -x$

A	A_4	B	B_4
(4, 5)	(−5, −4)	(−5, 4)	(−4, 5)
(5, 1)	(−1, −5)	(−5, 1)	(−1, 5)
(1, 2)	(−2, −1)	(−2, 2)	(−2, 2)
(a, b)	$(-b, -a)$	(a, b)	$(-b, -a)$

5. A rotation of 90° clockwise about the origin.

A	A_1	B	B_1
(4, 5)	(5, −4)	(−5, 4)	(4, 5)
(5, 1)	(1, −5)	(−5, 1)	(1, 5)
(1, 2)	(2, −1)	(−2, 2)	(2, 2)
(a, b)	$(b, -a)$	(a, b)	$(b, -a)$

6. A rotation of 180° about the origin.

A	A₂	B	B₂
(4, 5)	(−4, −5)	(−5, 4)	(5, −4)
(5, 1)	(−5, −1)	(−5, 1)	(5, −1)
(1, 2)	(−1, −2)	(−2, 2)	(2, −2)
(a, b)	(−a, −b)	(a, b)	(−a, −b)

7. A rotation of 270° clockwise about the origin.

A	A₃	B	B₃
(4, 5)	(−5, 4)	(−5, 4)	(−4, −5)
(5, 1)	(−1, 5)	(−5, 1)	(−1, −5)
(1, 2)	(−2, 1)	(−2, 2)	(−2, −2)
(a, b)	(−b, a)	(a, b)	(−b, a)

8. A rotation of 90° anticlockwise about the origin.

A	A₄	B	B₄
(4, 5)	(−5, 4)	(−5, 4)	(−4, −5)
(5, 1)	(−1, 5)	(−5, 1)	(−1, −5)
(1, 2)	(−2, 1)	(−2, 2)	(−2, −2)
(a, b)	(−b, a)	(a, b)	(−b, a)

9. An enlargement of scale factor 2 and centre of enlargement (0, 0)

A	A₅	B	B₅
(4, 5)	(8, 10)	(−5, 4)	(−10, 8)
(5, 1)	(10, 2)	(−5, 1)	(−10, 2)
(1, 2)	(2, 4)	(−2, 2)	(−4, 4)
(a, b)	(2a, 2b)	(a, b)	(2a, 2b)

10. Check pupils' own investigations.

Exercise 16.8: Summary exercise

1.
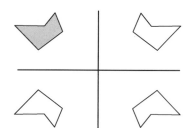

2.
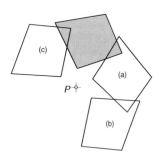

3. (a) (i) 2   (ii) 2   (iii) 4   (iv) none(1)   (v) none(1)
    (b) (i) 2   (ii) 2   (iii) 4   (iv) 1   (v) 1
    (c) Example

4.

5. (a) a translation by the vector $\begin{pmatrix} 5 \\ -5 \end{pmatrix}$

    (b) a rotation of 180° about the origin
    (c) a reflection in the line $y = x$
    (d) an enlargement of scale factor 3 and centre (−1, 1)

6. (a) and (b)

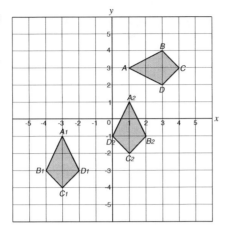

(c) a translation by the vector $\begin{pmatrix} 4 \\ 2 \end{pmatrix}$

End of chapter 16 activity: Hexaflexagons

Practical

Chapter 17: Ratio and proportion

In this chapter we first look at the ratio of areas and volumes after enlargement and then give some practice with harder problems involving ratios.

Exercise 17.1

1.	(a) 6 cm	(b) 36 cm²	(c) 1 : 4
2.	(a) 12 cm	(b) 144 cm²	(c) 1 : 9
3.	(a) 12 cm	(b) 144 cm²	(c) 1 :16
4.	(a) 1 cm	(b) 1 cm²	(c) 4 : 1
5.	(a) 6 cm and 8 cm	(b) 48 cm²	(c) 1 : 4
6.	(a) 15 cm and 18 cm	(b) 270 cm²	(c) 1 : 9
7.	(a) 24 cm and 15cm	(b) 180cm²	(c) 1 : 9
8.	(a) 40 cm	(b) 384 cm²	(c) 1 : 16
9.	672 cm²		
10.	756 cm²		
11.	6 cm		
12.	6 cm		

Exercise 17.2

1.	(a) 8 cm³	(b) 1 : 8	
2.	(a) 16 cm³	(b) 1 : 8	
3.	(a) 8 cm³	(b) 216 cm³	(c) 1 : 27
4.	(a) 135 cm³	(b) 1 : 27	
5.	3 cm³		
6.	24 cm³		

Exercise 17.3

1. Due to students' own measurements answers may vary a little.
    (a) 1 cm represents 25 cm
        1 m is represented by 4 cm
    (b) (i)   length 1 m; width 75 cm
        (ii)   length 2.125 m; width 85 cm
        (iii) 1.25 m
    (c) (i)   7500 cm² (0.75 m²)
        (ii)   18 062.5 cm² (1.81 m²)
        (iii) 6750 cm² (0.675 m²)
    (d) Approximately £225
    (e) A rectangle 6 cm by 8 cm (drawn on worksheet)
    (f) Approximately 0.3 m³
    (g) 3 m

2.	(a) 5 m	(b) 250 cm³	(c) 4 m

3. (a) Smallest jug contains 0.25 litres
Second contains $0.25 \times 1.25^3 = 0.49$ litres
Third contains $0.25 \times 1.5^3 = 0.84$ litres
Fourth contains $0.25 \times 1.75^3 = 1.34$ litres
Largest contains $0.25 \times 2^3 = 2$ litres
(b) 15.9 cm (to 1 d.p) volume of 1.0049 litres

4. (a) 2.55 m   (b) 2.55 cm   (c) 200 cm³
(d) 80 m² (work with full value in the calculator and the pi cancels out)
(e) 80 cm²

5. (a) 450 cm²   (b) 120 cm   (c) 1.5 litres

Exercise 17.4

1.

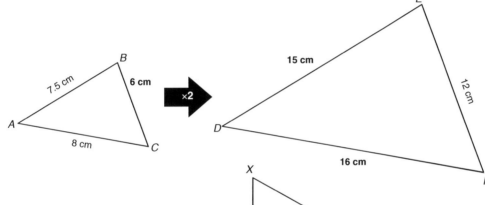

2.

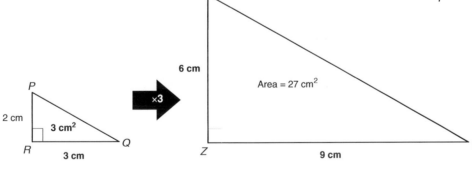

3.

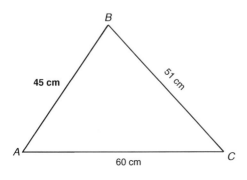

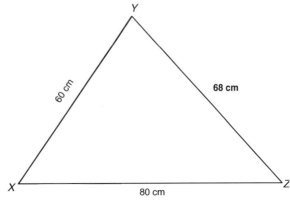

4.

Area of the object : area of the image is 4 : 9

5.

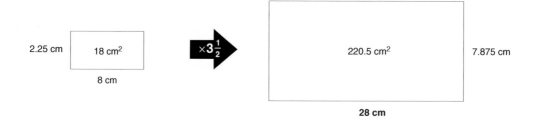

Exercise 17.5

1. 21

2. $13\frac{1}{3}$ (13.33)

3. 22.75
4. 63p

5. $17\frac{1}{2}$ cups

6. 10 500
7. 1920 kg
8. (a) 630 cm   (b) 158.73
9. 63 g
10. Bertha 14 and Alf 22

Exercise 17.6: Extension questions

1. (c) a pair of spheres,
and
(e) a pair of regular tetrahedra.

2. 125

3. (a) Surface area is $4A$ or $4\pi r^2$ and volume is $8V$ or $8\pi r^3$

    (b) Surface area is $\frac{4}{9}A$ or $\frac{4}{9}\pi r^2$ and volume is $\frac{8}{27}V$ or $\frac{8}{27}\pi r^3$

    (c) (i) Surface area of **S** : Surface area of **U** is 1 : 9

        (ii) Volume **S** : Volume **U** is 1 : 27

4. (a) $9A$ (b) 1 : 9   (c) $4A$, 1 : 4 : 9
    (d) $8V$, $27V$ (e) 1 : 8 : 27   (f) 1 : 7 : 19

5. (a) 32 cm³
    (b) (i) 256 cm³   (ii) 6912 cm³

Exercise 17.7: Summary exercise

1. (a) 10 cm   (b) 100 cm²   (c) 1 : 25
2. (a) 27 cm³   (b) 216 cm³   (c) 1 : 8
3. 6 cm³
4. $k = 3$, $x = 2\frac{2}{3}$ cm, $y = 9$ cm, $z = 27$ cm

5. (a) 35 euros   (b) £28.57
6. (a) $4h$ cm   (b) $16A$ cm²   (c) 1 : 64, 1 : 63

End of chapter 17 activity: Fibonacci and the Golden ratio

Examples of flowers:

3 petals: Lily, iris
                   Often lilies have 6 petals formed from two sets of 3.

4 petals: Very few plants show 4 petals (or sepals) but some, such as the fuchsia, do. 4 is *not* a
                   Fibonacci number! We return to this point near the bottom of this page.

5 petals: Buttercup, wild rose, larkspur, columbine (aquilegia), pinks.
                   The humble buttercup has been bred into a multi–petalled form.

8 petals: Delphiniums

13 petals: Ragwort, corn marigold, cineraria, some daisies

21 petals: Aster, black–eyed susan, chicory

34 petals: Plantain, pyrethrum

55, 89 petals: Michaelmas daisies, the asteraceae family.

Some species are very precise about the number of petals they have – for example buttercups. But others have petals that are very near those above with the average being a Fibonacci number.

Chapter 18: Introducing trigonometry

This chapter introduces trigonometry in terms of the tangent of an angle. It treats the tangent as the ratio of the opposite and adjacent sides.

Exercise 18.1

1.-5. The answers depend entirely on the size of the angle in the pupils' own drawings. The important thing to check is that $\tan BAC = \dfrac{BC}{AB}$

Check the correct use of terminology: The marking of the sides O, A and H follows on from the marking of H in the chapter on Pythagoras. Getting into the habit of marking all three sides from the very beginning will make everybody's lives much easier when you start dealing with a mixture of triangles and ratios.

Exercise 18.2

1.	1.73	**5.**	0.364	**9.**	3.17
2.	1	**6.**	0.521	**10.**	0.0875
3.	5.67	**7.**	2.14	**11.**	0.658
4.	0.268	**8.**	2.41	**12.**	0.956

Exercise 18.3

1.	56.3°	**5.**	26.6°	**9.**	77.5°
2.	66.5°	**6.**	60.3°	**10.**	89.4°
3.	35.8°	**7.**	41.7°	**11.**	2.9°
4.	8.0°	**8.**	20.3°	**12.**	17.7°

Exercise 18.4

1. $a = 3.22$ cm
2. $b = 22.5$ cm
3. $c = 45.0$ cm
4. $d = 1.291$ km
5. $e = 8.98$ m
6. $f = 26.1$ cm
7. $g = 1.36$ cm
8. $h = 24.4$ m
9. $i = 13.6$ mm
10. $j = 2.80$ m
11. Check pupils' drawings $BC = 6.48$ cm
12. Check pupils' drawings $EF = 855$ m

13.	Check pupils' drawings	$YZ = 47.7$ m
14.	Check pupils' drawings	$QR = 1.57$ m
15.	Check pupils' drawings	$ST = 107$ m

Exercise 18.5

1. $a = 15.6$ cm
2. $b = 28.3$ cm
3. $c = 7.51$ cm
4. $d = 117$ mm
5. $e = 3.89$ m
6. $f = 2.33$ km
7. $g = 34.1$ m
8. $h = 210$ m

9. $i = 0.699$ m
10. $j = 41.7$ cm
11. $k = 9.23$ cm
12. $l = 6.72$ m
13. $m = 5.76$ km
14. $n = 20.0$ cm

15. $BC = 93.3$ cm
16. $DF = 19.6$ m
17. $XZ = 13.6$ km
18. $QR = 3.67$ m

Exercise 18.6

1. $a = 63.4°$
2. $b = 39.8°$
3. $c = 17.5°$
4. $d = 16.7°$
5. $e = 48.4°$
6. $f = 55.0°$
7. $g = 67.4°$
8. $h = 75.6°$
9. $i = 18.9°$
10. $j = 13.1°$

11. $\angle A = 68.2°$
12. $\angle D = 57.4°$
13. $\angle X = 26.6°$
14. $\angle P = 56.0°$
15. $\angle C = 25.6°$

Exercise 18.7

1. 4.37 m
2. 7.13 m
3. 80.0 m
4. 678 m
5. 38.7°
6. 18.4°

Exercise 18.8: Extension questions

1. 60 units
2. Pupils' own measurements should be approximately:

Angle *AOB*	*AB*	$\dfrac{AB}{60}$
15°	16 mm	0.3
30°	35 mm	0.6
45°	60 mm	1
60°	104 mm	1.7
75°	224 mm	3.7

3. Getting larger and tan 90° is infinity.
4. Check pupils' own graphs. The measurements should be approximately:
   (a) 0.4   (b) 1.4   (c) 2.1   (d) 5.7
5. Pupils should have checked their answers to q.4 with a calculator.
   (a) 0.364   (b) 1.43   (c) 2.14   (d) 5.67

Exercise 18.9: Summary exercise

1. (a) 0.445   (b) 1.28   (c) 3.08
2. (a) $x = 31.0°$ (b) $x = 51.1°$ (c) $x = 74.9°$
3. $a = 1.77$ m $b = 90.1$ mm
4. 34.3°
5. $XZ = 21.4$ cm
6. $BC = 1.74$ m
7. $\angle D = 64.4°$
8. 66.6 m

End of chapter 18 activity: The cube root trick

Practical

Chapter 19: More trigonometry

This chapter extends trigonometry to include sine and cosine. Emphasis is placed on using correct methods and setting out the calculations carefully. Focusing on this at this stage will make it easier to tackle the final mixed problems successfully.

The origin of the word 'sine' is an interesting piece of mathematical history.

Exercise 19.1: Sine and cosine

1.-5. The answers will depend on the pupils' own drawings. The important thing to check is that

$$\sin BAC = \frac{BC}{AC} \quad \text{and} \quad \cos BAC = \frac{AB}{AC}$$

Exercise 19.2

1.	0.5	**5.**	0.342	**9.**	0.976
2.	0.259	**6.**	0.793	**10.**	0.0872
3.	0.174	**7.**	0.996	**11.**	0.288
4.	0.906	**8.**	0.976	**12.**	0.897

Exercise 19.3

1.
(a) 44.4°
(b) 64.2°
(c) 30°
(d) 11.5°

(e) 48.6°
(f) 6.9°
(g) 62.9°
(h) 21.7°

(i) 34.5°
(j) 20.2°
(k) 3.2°
(l) 22.5°

2.
(a) 45.6°
(b) 25.8°
(c) 60°
(d) 78.5°

(e) 41.4°
(f) 83.1°
(g) 27.1°
(h) 68.3°

(i) 55.5°
(j) 69.8°
(k) 86.8°
(l) 67.5°

3. angle q.1(a) + angle q.2(a) is 90°
angle q.1(b) + angle q.2(b) is 90°   etc…

Finding opposite and adjacent sides using sine and cosine

The method of writing H, O and A and then crossing out the letter you do not need, can be very useful in helping to work out which ratio to use.

Exercise 19.4

1. $b = 16.1$ m
2. $c = 11.5$ mm
3. $d = 33.3$ cm
4. $e = 1.11$ km
5. $f = 3.83$ m
6. $g = 19.0$ cm
7. $k = 0.892$ km
8. $j = 14.8$ mm
9. $k = 1.87$ m
10. $l = 38.8$ mm

11. $m = 5.32$ cm
12. $n = 43.5$ m
13. $p = 1.30$ mm
14. $q = 85.1$ cm
15. $AB = 2.56$ km
16. $DE = 6.70$ m
17. $YZ = 25.7$ cm
18. $KL = 44.0$ m
19. $RQ = 154$ mm
20. $SU = 2.43$ m

Exercise 19.5

1. $b = 8.97$ cm
2. $c = 4.04$ m
3. $d = 6.98$ km
4. $e = 1.63$ m
5. $f = 19.1$ cm

6. $g = 84.9$ cm
7. $AC = 9.57$ cm
8. $DE = 13.2$ m
9. $XY = 6.28$ km
10. $PQ = 33.8$ mm

Exercise 19.6

1. $a = 39.8°$
2. $b = 53.1°$
3. $c = 22.6°$
4. $d = 45.6°$
5. $e = 41.8°$
6. $f = 26.8°$
7. $g = 67.2°$
8. $h = 47.9°$
9. $i = 55.2°$

10. $j = 38.7°$
11. $k = 45.6°$
12. $l = 50.9°$
13. $m = 23.6°$
14. $n = 51.6°$
15. $\angle A = 44.4°$
16. $\angle D = 67.5°$
17. $\angle Y = 78.8°$
18. $\angle P = 28.7°$

Exercise 19.7

1. 12.4 m
2. 10.7 km
3. 81.9 km
4. 217°, 8.77 m
5. 63.4°, 20.1

6. (a) $WY = 9.16$ m   (b) $\angle XYZ = 35°$ (c) $XZ = 4.30$ m   (d) $WX = 5.25$ m

7. (a) 171 miles North and 470 miles West   (b) 287 miles West and 410 miles South

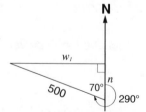

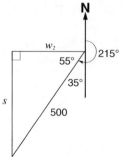

(c)

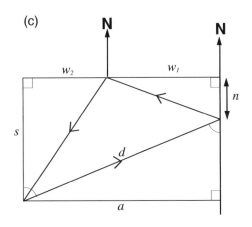

(d) 72.5°, 794 miles

Extension Exercise 19.8

1.   (a)

  (b) $\sqrt{3}$

  (c) $\sin 30° = \dfrac{1}{2}$, $\cos 30° = \dfrac{\sqrt{3}}{2}$ and $\tan 30° = \dfrac{1}{\sqrt{3}}$ or $\dfrac{\sqrt{3}}{3}$

  (d) $\sin 60° = \dfrac{\sqrt{3}}{2}$, $\cos 60° = \dfrac{1}{2}$ and $\tan 60° = \sqrt{3}$

2.   (a)

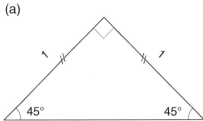

  (b) $\sqrt{2}$

  (c) $\sin 45° = \dfrac{1}{\sqrt{2}}$ or $\dfrac{\sqrt{2}}{2}$, $\cos 45° = \dfrac{1}{\sqrt{2}}$ or $\dfrac{\sqrt{2}}{2}$ and $\tan 45° = 1$

3. $\sin a = \dfrac{3}{5}$, $\cos a = \dfrac{4}{5}$ and $\tan a = \dfrac{3}{4}$

$\sin b = \dfrac{5}{13}$, $\cos b = \dfrac{12}{13}$ and $\tan b = \dfrac{5}{12}$

4.

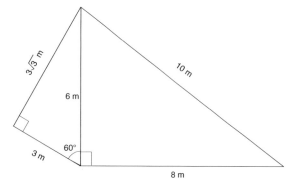

5. 140 m

6. $AB = 240 - \dfrac{100}{\sqrt{3}} = 182.3$ m, $AD = 260$ m.

Exercise 19.9: Summary exercise

1. (a) 1.11   (b) 0.788   (c) 0.469

2. (a) 56.3°   (b) 51.7°   (c) 50.8°

3. (a) 0.821 m   (c) 15.0 cm
     (b) 1.01 km   (d) 47.3 cm

4. (a) 55.2°   (b) 30.8°

5. $KL = 44$ m
6. $DE = 28.4$ m
7. $\angle Y = 78.8°$
8. 84.5 km

End of chapter 19 activity: Binary arithmetic

1. 6   **6.** 13
2. 3   **7.** 7
3. 11   **8.** 10
4. 21   **9.** 29
5. 25   **10.** 63

11. 1000   **16.** 10 000
12. 10 011   **17.** 10 100
13. 110 010   **18.** 1 100 100
14. 101 000 100   **19.** 10 101 011
15. 110 101 101   **20.** 11 110 101

Chapter 20: Looking at data

This chapter revises the methods of looking at data in **Maths** Prep Book 2 and extends the level of questions to include 'real life' data, which often does not involve convenient numbers.

This chapter may be usefully covered before geography fieldwork. Several of the examples are deliberately based on geography projects.

Exercise 20.1

1. A pie chart to show the reasons people come to the park

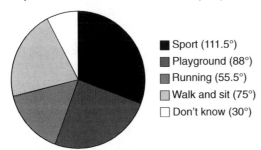

■ Sport (111.5°)
■ Playground (88°)
■ Running (55.5°)
☐ Walk and sit (75°)
☐ Don't know (30°)

2. A pie chart to show the distribution of litter found in the park

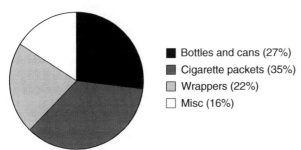

■ Bottles and cans (27%)
■ Cigarette packets (35%)
☐ Wrappers (22%)
☐ Misc (16%)

Exercise 20.2

1. A bar chart to show the length of time people spent in the park in the morning

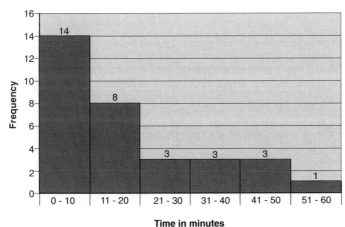

Time in minutes

2. A bar char to show the length of time people spent in the park in the early evening

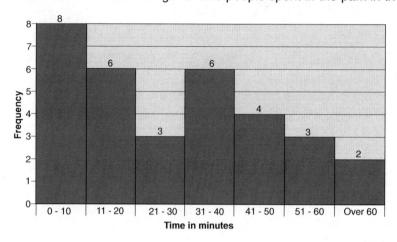

3. In the morning, more people spent shorter periods of time in the park. This may be because they were passing through it on the way to somewhere else (work, shopping etc) or it may be small children spending a short time playing in the park.

In the early evening it is more likely that adults would be going to the park, to jog or run, or relax after a day's work. Older children might go to play football. Probably fewer people would come and just sit because it might be cooler.

Exercise 20.3

1. A scatter graph to show the results of our survey to find out the maximum price people would consider paying in order to go into the park

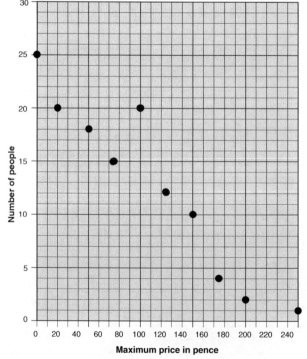

The graph shows negative correlation.

2. (a) A scatter graph to show the results of a survey looking at the recorded midday temperatures and the number of people who used the park in the early evening

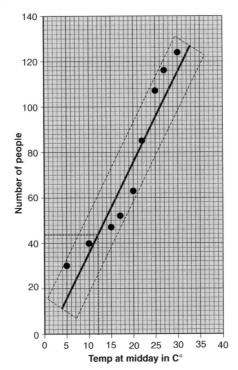

Number of people

Temp at midday in C°

(b) Line of best fit
(c) Positive correlation
(d) 44 people

Exercise 20.4

1. (a) Range = 7 − 1 = 6

Mean = $3\frac{1}{3}$

Mode = 2
Median = 2.5

(b) Range = 2.6 − 1.2 = 1.4
Mean = 1.68
Mode = 1.2 and 1.5
Median = 1.5

(c) Range = 95 − 25 = 70
Mean = 64.5
Mode none
Median = 67

(d) Range = 42 − 34 = 8
Mean = 38.6
Mode = 37.5
Median = 39

2. Check the pupils' own suggestions. Here are some examples:
    (a) number of seeds in a grape; scores on an octagonal spinner
    (b) increase in height in cm grown by bean plants in a week; lengths of beetles in cm
    (c) ages in years of people on a bus; ages in years of people in a hospital ward
    (d) height in cm of new born baby; time to the nearest $\frac{1}{2}$ sec of runners in a 200 m race

3. I am 14

4. 1.5 m

5. (a) Range = 3.1 – 0 = 3.1
        Mean = 1.5
        Mode = 1.5
        Median = 1.5

(b)

Rainfall in cm	Tally	Frequency
0 – 0.4	︱︱︱︱	5
0.5 – 0.9	︱︱	2
1.0 – 1.4	︱︱︱︱	5
1.5 – 1.9	︱︱︱︱ ︱︱︱︱	9
2.0 – 2.4	︱︱︱︱	4
2.5 – 2.9	︱︱︱︱	4
3.0 – 3.4	︱	1
		30

A frequency diagram to show the daily rainfall in September

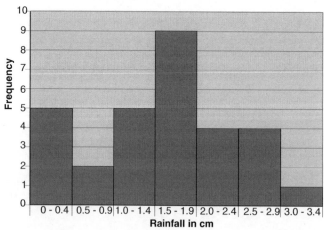

(c) The mean, mode and median were all 1.5 cm. It rained on most days.
(d) There was more rainfall than in April, it rained on more days and rained more – the mean rainfall is significantly higher.

6. (a) – (b)

No of seeds	Frequency	Angle
2	2	14°
3	10	72°
4	13	94°
5	16	115°
6	6	43°
7	3	22°
Total	50	360°

(c) A pie chart to show the number of seeds found in seed pods

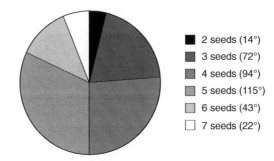

- 2 seeds (14°)
- 3 seeds (72°)
- 4 seeds (94°)
- 5 seeds (115°)
- 6 seeds (43°)
- 7 seeds (22°)

(d) The mode was 5 seeds, most had 4, 5 or 6 seeds, a few had 2 or 3, and a few had 7

7. The range of the number of seeds was less (5) in the wetter environment.

The mode and the median in the wetter environment was 2, in the drier environment the mode was 5 and the median 4.5 and the mean was 4.46. (We cannot calculate the mean in the wetter environment.)

8. (a) – (b)

No of nectarines	Frequency	Angle
18	3	27°
19	5	45°
20	9	81°
21	14	126°
22	6	54°
23	3	27°
Total	40	360°

Range = 23 – 18 = 5
Mean = 20.6
Mode = 21
Median = 21

(b) You can work out the mean, 20

9. The most significant difference is in beef sales. There are more sales at supermarket B than at supermarket A. There is marginally more pork and poultry sold at A than at B, and lamb is about the same. Perhaps supermarket B is in an area where wealthier people live, those who have more money to spend on shopping. Beef is more expensive than most other meat whereas chicken and pork are cheaper.

10. You might be able to assume that month A could be December because it shows more poultry (the Christmas turkey) and more pork (the Christmas ham) being sold.

11. Check pupils' own questions

12. (a) A scatter graph to compare the number of hours spent revising to the positions achieved in the examinations

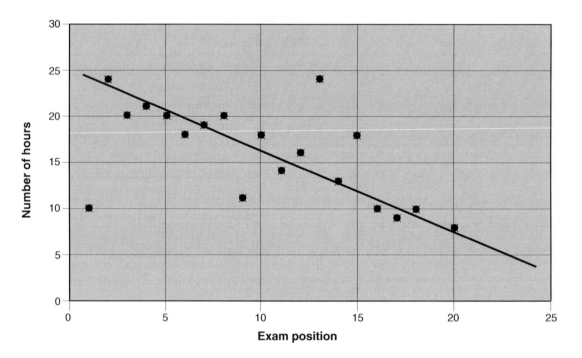

The graph shows a negative correlation. The smaller the amount of revision done, the lower the exam position achieved. (Note: Pupils may draw the graph with exam position on the *y*-axis and number of hours on the *x*-axis)

(b) The percentage against number of hours.

(c) The person who came top with ten hours revision could have just been brilliant. Some people might revise for a long time but still not be able to remember in exams. Some people might no tell the truth (it is uncool to be seen to be working hard). Other reasons could be illness during the exam, revision of the wrong material or poor revision technique.

Exercise 20.5

1. (a) A frequency diagram to show the results of a survey that looked at the ages of passengers taking the Eurostar train to Paris on a weekday

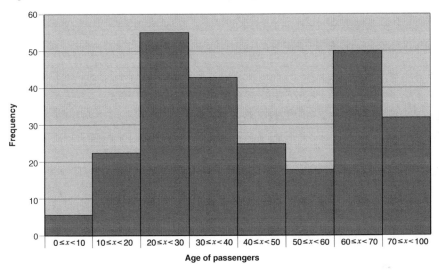

(b) They would be at school or college.
(c) Perhaps there are special discount for over 60s. They also have more free time.

2. (a) The results of a survey that looked at the ages of passengers taking the Eurostar train to Paris at the weekend

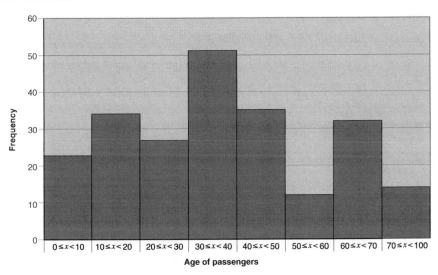

(b) There are more young passengers and fewer old ones.

Exercise 20.6

1.

No. in house	Tally	Frequency	Total people
2	II	2	2 × 2 = 4
3	IIII	4	3 × 4 = 12
4	‖‖ III	8	4 × 8 = 32
5	‖‖ II	7	5 × 7 = 35
6	III	3	6 × 3 = 18
7	I	1	7 × 1 = 7
Total		25	108

Mean = $\dfrac{108}{25}$ = 4.32

Mode = 4
Median = 4

2. (a) (i) If $x = 8$ mode = 4, median = 4
   (ii) If $x = 9$ mode = 3 and 4, median = 3.5
   (iii) If $x = 10$ mode = 3, median = 3
(b) $x = 5$, mode = 4, median = 4

3. (a) 20 and 25
(b) 25 min
(c) 25 min
(d)

Time in mins	Frequency
0–5	7
6–10	16
11–15	17
16–20	20
21–25	17
26–30	14
31–35	12
36–40	11
41–45	9
46–50	7
51–55	5
56–60	2
Total	137

(e) A frequency diagram to show the journey times to school

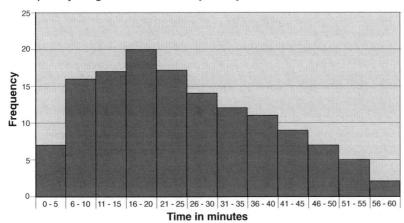

(f) 137
(g) 16 – 20 minutes

4. (a) Holidays usually go in weeks and a week is 7 days.
    (b) One who comes from abroad, like an Australian or a young teacher who likes travelling.
    (c) 19.2 days (for a total of 808 days and 42 teachers)
    (d) 20.6 days

5. (a) A frequency chart to show the amount of money raised in a Readathon

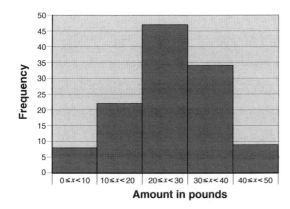

(b) $5 \times 8 + 15 \times 22 + 25 \times 47 + 35 \times 34 + 45 \times 9 = £3140$

Exercise 20.7: Summary exercise

1. (a) Range = 5 – 1 = 4
        Mean = 2.6
        Median = 2.5
        Mode = 1

    (b) Range = 5.8 – 1.2 = 4.6
        Mean = 3.8
        Median = 4.2
        Mode = 4.2

    (c) Range = $3\frac{1}{2} - 1\frac{3}{4} = 1\frac{3}{4}$
        Mean = 2.65
        Median = $2\frac{1}{2}$
        Mode = none

2.   (a) 12 min 12 sec   (b) 11 min 58 sec

3.   (a)

Height in cm	Frequency
0–9	5
10–19	3
20–29	9
30–39	9
40–49	4
total	30

A frequency chart to show the heights of bean plants

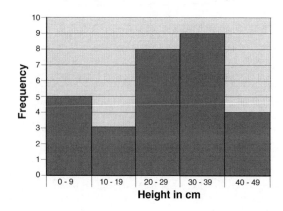

Range = 48 – 0 = 48
Mean = 25.5
Median = 26.5
Modal group = 31–40

(b) Most plants grew well, in a small range of 23–48, 5 did not grow at all and 3 grew less than 20 cm
(c) The modal group does not change, the mean becomes 30.6 and the median is 31
(d) Yes, the plants should be included in the results. It is important to know that some plants may not grow.

4.   Mean = 20 351
          Mode = 14 000
          Median = 18 000
(a) Mean – but it depends on your salary
(b) Median
(c) Mean

5.   Check the pupils' own answers.

End of chapter 20 activity: Data collection

Practical